TWOPENCE TO CROSS THE MERSEY

HELEN FORRESTER

Adapted by
Valerie Windsor

Resource Material
Cecily O'Neill

Series Consultant
Cecily O'Neill

COLLINS EDUCATIONAL

Collins Educational, 8 Grafton Street, London W1X 3LA
© Playscript, Helen Forrester and Valerie Windsor, end-material
Cecily O'Neil
First published 1987
Reprinted 1988, 1989, 1990

ISBN 0 00 330236 9

Cover design by the Pinpoint Design Co.

All photographs courtesy of the BBC Hulton Picture Library
Typesetting by CG Graphics, Aylesbury, Bucks
Printed and bound in Great Britain by Bell and Bain, Glasgow.

CONTENTS

THE CHARACTERS

Helen
Mother
Father
Grandmother
Alan
Fiona
Brian
Tony
Avril
Landlady at Brewer Street
Clerk
Man behind
Woman at door
Mrs Foster
Mrs Foster's brother
Spanish woman
Mr Moritz
Young policeman
Man at Pier Head
Fish-shop assistant
Mr Grimshaw
The old gentleman
Public assistance officer
Charity worker
Teacher
Art teacher
Nurse
Man (Peter Molloy)
Sailor

Various neighbours, children, men in queues, women at pawn shop, children at school etc.

Most small parts can be doubled.

TWOPENCE TO CROSS THE MERSEY

Act I
SCENE ONE

The Pier Head, Liverpool. **Helen Forrester** *stands looking out over the River Mersey.*

HELEN   *as* **Narrator**, *remembering*   The Pier Head.
Liverpool. The times I stood here looking across . . . That's
Birkenhead over there, look . . . There's the Cammel Laird
shipyards . . .
   It used to cost twopence to cross the Mersey. Two whole
pennies. I never had that much. All I could ever do was
dream. Beyond Birkenhead . . . over there beyond all those
buildings . . . is the Wirral peninsula. Lovely green
countryside . . . farms . . . little villages. My grandmother
lived in the Wirral. I used to dream of catching the ferry
and going across to visit her . . . Clean sheets on the bed and
the smell of lavender polish and fresh bread . . . 'Look
what's happened to us, Granny,' I'd say. 'Please let me stay
here with you.' Except of course I never had the twopence
for the ferry fare and even if I had . . . *She shrugs sadly* . . .
I don't know. I don't know whether she'd have wanted to see
me.
   They'd quarrelled, you see. Alan and I heard it. The little
ones were all asleep but we crept out onto the landing and
listened. We were dreadfully frightened. So many odd
things had been happening. Mother's wonderful collection of
Georgian silver, for example. One day it just vanished.

Alan *joins* **Helen***. The pier head becomes the staircase in the
Forresters' large, comfortable house somewhere in the south of
England. Below them, in the drawing room, are* **Helen's
parents** *and her* **Grandmother***.*

ALAN   *as he joins* **Helen**, *whispering*   Perhaps it's been
sold.

1

They squat down as if listening through the bannisters. They are both wide-eyed with fear.

HELEN Why?

ALAN I don't know. Helen, there's something awfully wrong. Mary Anne's packing her suitcase.

HELEN She's going home for a few days . . . for a visit. To see her mother.

BRIAN That's not what she said to Cook. And then Cook said something about rats leaving sinking ships. What's that mean?

HELEN Sssh!

Below them the adults start to speak.

GRANDMOTHER *extremely angry* Yes, you see, that just about sums it up, doesn't it? You've drifted on as you always have done, expecting money to be there when you wanted it . . .

FATHER Mother . . .

GRANDMOTHER Doing not a hand's turn. When I think how hard your father worked. Twenty years old when he first came to Liverpool and he worked his way up until he was one of the city's most respected businessmen . . .

FATHER Look . . .

GRANDMOTHER Everything he possibly could do he did for you. The best of everything. The best schools . . .

FATHER Yes, I know . . .

GRANDMOTHER And what did you do with it all? Nothing. Absolutely nothing. You could have gone to university. You were a brilliant scholar. Goodness knows why you never pursued an academic career. Your headmaster at All Saints . . .

MOTHER Oh, not All Saints again! Precious All Saints!

GRANDMOTHER *ignoring her* . . . told me you would have sailed through the Oxford Entrance . . .

FATHER There was the small matter of the War, Mother, don't forget.

GRANDMOTHER Don't try being sarcastic with me, John.

FATHER It's just that this is all old ground. We've been over all this. What I want . . .

2

GRANDMOTHER Yes, that's it, isn't it? That's it. What *you* want. And what about what *I* wanted? I'd hoped that after such an excellent schooling, you would have found a decent post in the city and done well, but oh no. Nothing like that.

FATHER That's not true. It was simply that Celia and I felt . . .

GRANDMOTHER Ah, now we're getting to the root of things, aren't we?

MOTHER Oh, here we go again. All my fault. If it hadn't been for me, etc. etc. Go on, say it. Say it. You've been itching to for years.

GRANDMOTHER I see you're pregnant again, Celia.

MOTHER Yes.

GRANDMOTHER Well, if that isn't the height of irresponsibility, then I really don't know what is.

FATHER *desperately trying to calm the atmosphere* Look, Mother, if you could just lend us enough to get us straight. Say three thousand . . .

Grandmother makes a noise indicating that such a loan is out of the question.

MOTHER No, listen to him. Please.

GRANDMOTHER No, John, I'm sorry. My lawyer is quite adamant about this. The estate won't stand any more. I advise you to begin by selling some of the contents of this house . . .

FATHER *almost in tears* Please, Mother. If not for us, then for the children . . .

MOTHER Oh, don't grovel. You can see she's made up her mind. God knows what you expected from her. She always was a tight-fisted, sanctimonious old biddy. No wonder your father . . .

FATHER *horrified* Celia! Oh, look, Mother, I apologise.

MOTHER For goodness sake!

GRANDMOTHER *furious* No, no, no. Please don't bother. It's what I expected. Perhaps you'd be kind enough to ring for a taxi. I shall find a hotel for the night. I prefer not to stay where I'm so unwelcome. You've been a disappointment to me all your life, John. I wash my hands of you. Of the pair of you . . . *And she sweeps out of the room.*

Helen *stands up. As she speaks,* **Alan** *goes to join the rest of the family assembling below.*

HELEN *narrating* We'd always lived in Bramwash. All my life. I didn't know anything else. The doll's house in the nursery, 'Children's Hour' on the radio, Nanny reading to us at bedtime. School, which I liked. Dancing class, which I loved. Riding. That terrified me. I was afraid of breaking my glasses. We didn't see much of our parents. They were always busy . . . tennis parties, bridge parties, holidays in London, weekends in the country with friends. They had a lot of friends. Literary, artistic people. None of them seemed to do any work. I suppose my parents must have lived on the income from inherited money, but what little capital my father had left was invested in cotton companies . . . He never really understood financial matters . . . and when Wall Street crashed . . .

First one thing went and then another. The pony. The books. The pictures in the hall. My mother's jewellery. Then the kitchen maid left, taking most of my mother's clothes with her. Instead of wages, I suppose. Then Cook left. Then Nanny . . . The debts mounted up.

When the end came, my mother was in hospital. Brian had just been born and she was very ill. 'We're going to live in Liverpool', my father told us. 'That's where I used to live when I was a little boy. That's where our family made their fortune. We'll soon get back on our feet once we're in Liverpool.'

SCENE TWO

Helen *comes down to join the rest of the family, who are sitting in the waiting room of Lime Street Station. The* **mother** *lies along one of the benches. The* **children***, with the exception of* **Avril***, who is fidgeting, sit in nervous silence.*

HELEN *narrating* Lime Street Station, Liverpool. It was 4th January, 1931. I was twelve and a half years old and understood enough of what was happening to be afraid. I was wearing my velour school hat . . . St Catherine's School for Girls . . . and my new school coat. My mother had only left hospital that morning: she'd discharged herself . . . slipped out when no one was looking. Well, there was no money left to pay the hospital bill. There was no money left for anything. The creditors had taken it all: our clothes, the rest of the furniture, everything. We had nothing left but what we stood up in.

FATHER *anxiously: he can see that she is in pain* Are you all right, Celia?

MOTHER *through gritted teeth* Yes.

AVRIL I'm hungry. Daddy, I'm hungry.

FATHER As soon as we've found somewhere to stay we'll get a doctor.

MOTHER *breathing out as the pain subsides* Don't be absurd. What'll we pay him with? Do stop whining, Avril. Helen, make her sit still. I still think if you'd explained the circumstances they'd have let us stay put for a while. Pammy Charteris says . . .

FATHER You haven't been discussing our affairs with Pammy Charteris!

MOTHER She says you're allowed all sorts of basic things. Your beds. They can't take your beds. And your clothes. Your personal things.

FATHER It's a matter of honour, Celia. If they foreclose on us, then everything belongs to them. The debt has to be paid.

MOTHER Oh, honour! What's honour? Never mind that. What about basic rights? *She's caught by a pain* Take the baby, Helen. *To* **Father** Oh for goodness' sake, stop wasting time. Go and find somewhere for us to sleep. And bring some cigarettes back with you. *She closes her eyes as the pain washes over her again.*

FATHER *drawing* **Helen** *aside* Look after her. Don't let the children bother her. I'll be as quick as I can. *He pulls his coat collar up against the cold and rain and hurries out.*

HELEN *narrating; quiet so as not to disturb mother* This is Edward, the baby. Only a few days old. This is Alan. That's Fiona. **Fiona,** *very quiet and frightened, sits clutching a teddy bear* With the one toy we were allowed to bring: she couldn't bear to be parted from it and no one could ever deny Fiona anything. She's the pretty one. That's Brian. That's Tony. And that . . . *Pointing to* **Avril,** *who is running about being a nuisance* That's Avril. Come on,

Avril. *She heaves **Avril** onto the bench beside her*   There's a good girl.

AVRIL   I'm cold.

MOTHER   Do stop her whining.

HELEN   *to **Avril***   We're all cold.

AVRIL   And I'm hungry.

MOTHER   What on earth is he doing all this time?

AVRIL   I haven't had anything to eat for . . .   *She makes a face to show an unimaginable length of time*   . . . years.

HELEN   *narrating*   Not since the previous night anyway. Things had happened too fast. Nobody had thought to buy anything. In our world food had simply appeared whenever it was time to eat.   *They sit in silence for a moment; **Brian** and **Tony** are asleep on each other's shoulders*   Hours passed. It was bitterly cold.

MOTHER   Helen, look in my handbag. I think there's one cigarette left . . .

*Cold and exhausted, **Mr Forrester** enters.*

MOTHER   *turning on him*   Where've you been? I was beginning to think we'd been deserted. 'Wife and Seven Children Abandoned on Lime Street Station'!

FATHER   *too exhausted to respond*   Don't start, Celia. Please. Not now.   *To the **children***   Come on. Up you get, Brian. Come on, Tony.

HELEN   Where are we going?

FATHER   I've found a couple of rooms . . .

MOTHER   What sort of rooms? Where?   *She struggles to stand up.*

FATHER   Just for a couple of weeks. Till we can find something better. It's about a mile away.

MOTHER   It's no good, John. I can't walk. We'll have to get a taxi.

*The family stragggle out of the waiting room. **Helen**, still holding the baby, brings up the rear. She pauses at the exit.*

HELEN   *narrating*   We caught glimpses of Liverpool through the streaming windows of a taxi. Water swirled along the gutters. Across the road, the pillars of St George's Hall looked like a row of rotting teeth. Black buildings.

Narrow streets. Pale men huddled up in thin ragged jackets
. . . slumped against walls. Unemployed miners from the
Rhondda begging on a street corner. And then the taxi drew
up outside a shabby, terraced house. Number twenty-three,
Brewer Street.

SCENE THREE

The **landlady**, *large and cheerful, bustles across to open the
door. She ushers them in.*

LANDLADY   I thought you must've got lost. Come in. Come
in. I said: That Mr Forrester, he'll have got lost. Still, I said,
not to worry, eh. Paid in advance, so what am I worrying
about? Watch out, love, there's a rotten board
there.   *Opening a door*   These are the rooms. Bit dirty,
like. Well, I haven't had time today. I wasn't expecting
tenants.

The smell makes **Fiona** *cough.*

LANDLADY   *suspiciously*   What's the matter with her?
She's not got a chest, has she?

FATHER   That's enough, Fiona.

LANDLADY   Through here . . . this is the bedroom . . .

MOTHER   *appalled*   What about sheets? And blankets?

LANDLADY   Tenants provide their own bedding, love. I
don't provide bedding.

MOTHER   Have you got any other pillows?

LANDLADY   What's the matter with them pillers?

MOTHER   They're filthy.

LANDLADY   *offended*   Oh, well, if the rooms don't suit . . .

FATHER   The rooms are fine. Thank you.

LANDLADY   Anyroad, I did them meself. You'll not find
cleaner. Half a tin of bloody Keating's powder in them
pillers.

MOTHER   Half a tin of what?

LANDLADY   Keating's powder, love. Freezing in here, in't
it?   *Going*   I'll send you up a bucket of coal, then you can
warm up a bit, make yourselves a nice cup of tea. He'll be
along in a minute, the coalman. You can pay me back then.

FATHER Thank you.

MOTHER *as soon as the landlady's gone* You paid the rent in advance? Without even consulting me?

FATHER *wearily* Celia, there was nowhere else.

MOTHER Nowhere else? In the whole of Liverpool?

FATHER I didn't try the whole of Liverpool.

MOTHER I can't stay here. Don't take your coats off, children. We're not staying. *To **father*** Say we want the money back.

FATHER I can't do that.

MOTHER The smell of these mattresses.

FATHER It's cheap.

MOTHER I should think it is.

FATHER Celia, she's the only one who didn't change her mind the moment she discovered there were seven children.

MOTHER How much money have you got left?

FATHER Two and nine.

MOTHER Two and nine! *For a moment it's uncertain whether she's going to laugh or cry. The **children** watch her, terrified. Then, in a small, frightened voice* What are we going to do?

FATHER It'll be all right. You're not to worry. I'll go to the employment offices tomorrow. We won't be here long.

LANDLADY *calling* Coal on the landing, Mr Forrester!

FATHER Thank you.

MOTHER Have you got any cigarettes?

FATHER There's a corner shop down the road. I'll get some.

MOTHER And some milk for Edward. And something to eat.

FATHER *going* Shan't be five minutes. *Giving **Helen** his matches* See if you can get a fire started, Helen.

MOTHER Where are we supposed to cook? On the fire? And where do we get water from?

*Mrs Forrester collapses onto the ragged settee. **Helen** is laying coals in the grate.*

ALAN There's a tap at the top of the stairs.

MOTHER   Get some water, Helen. And you'd better try and rinse out Edward's nappy.

AVRIL   I'm freezing.

HELEN   *irritably*   All right. Sssh! I don't know how to do it. It keeps going out.

ALAN   *who has found an old saucepan*   I'll get the water.

FIONA   When Mary Anne lit the nursery fire she used paper and sticks of wood.

HELEN   We haven't got any paper and sticks of wood. *She warns them not to disturb their **Mother**, who is lying back with her eyes closed*   Sssh.

MOTHER   *quietly, her eyes still closed*   We can't stay here. I am not sleeping in that bed.

*Mr Forrester comes with an armful of shopping. **Alan** follows with the water.*

FATHER   Here we are. One packet of cigarettes . . . milk for Edward . . . bread . . . margarine . . . sugar . . . sausages . . . pennyworth of tea. What's happened to that fire?

HELEN   It keeps going out.

FATHER   Let me have a go.

LANDLADY   *calling up*   Mr Forrester! The coalman's coming.

MOTHER   *without moving*   Coal. You'd better go and get some.

FATHER   I can't.

MOTHER   *irritated*   Why not?

FATHER   How do you think I bought all this? I've got . . . *He counts the change in his pocket*   a penny three farthings. No, Twopence.

MOTHER   But we must have coal. That won't last the evening.

FATHER   Where's that water? We'll make tea first. By the way, there's a school a bit further down the street. It looks all right. I could register the children tomorrow morning. Keep them out from under your feet.

MOTHER   *hopelessly*   I don't know what to do.

FATHER   Let me worry about it.

MOTHER   Small babies *must* be kept warm. They *must*.

FATHER   It's all right. I'll get coal tomorrow.

MOTHER   *verging on hysteria*   What with? What'll you buy it with? What are we going to buy food with? Oh God!

HELEN   *narrating*   We sat huddled round the tiny grate in our coats and ate a slice of bread and a sausage each. My mother ate nothing . . . only drank a great deal and smoked.

MOTHER   *hopelessly*   I don't know what to do.

FATHER   *hurrying the **children** out of the way*   Come on, children. Bedtime. Boys in one bed, girls in the other. Keep your underclothes on. Put your coats over you for warmth.

BRIAN   What about cleaning our teeth?

ALAN   There's a tap on the stairs.

FATHER   Better just wash hands and faces.

HELEN   *narrating, as **Mr Forrester** shepherds the **children** out*   That was the first of endless nights I spent unable to settle because of cold or hunger or the smell of stale urine. Avril kicked and Fiona coughed. I remember thinking, well at least tomorrow I'll be going to school. I liked school. I was good at school. And there'd be a warm stove there. Or radiators. It'll be all right, I thought. We won't have to stay here long. As soon as Daddy's got a job we'll buy a proper house . . . maybe somewhere in the country near Granny. I hope they have art lessons at this school, I thought. Art was my very best subject. But in the morning . . .

FATHER   *coming back in*   Come on, hurry up, Helen. Make some tea for your mother. She's going to need a lot of help today.

HELEN   But I'm going to school today. You said . . .

FATHER   *taking her aside*   Well, the thing is Helen, better not for a day or two. You'll be more useful here. It'll keep the others busy and out of the way. But Mummy'll need you to look after her and the baby. And Avril, of course.

HELEN   But you said . . . Daddy, I *want* to go to school.

FATHER   It's not going to be anything like St Catherine's.

HELEN   No, I know, but . . .

FATHER   As soon as I've got work you'll be going to a proper school. In the meantime, your mother needs . . . she's not well. She needs . . . Look, you don't want everyone to think you're being selfish, do you? **Helen** shakes her *head* There's a good girl. I'll see you as soon as I get back from the Employment office.

Helen *deals with the fire, puts the saucepan on to heat, feeds the* **baby**. *All this time* **Mrs Forrester** *lies on the broken sofa with her eyes shut.* **Avril** *plays on the floor. Both children are afraid of their mother's silence.*

SCENE FOUR

Meanwhile, **Mr Forrester** *has left the house. He is now in the Employment Office. A* **Clerk** *sits at a desk. A long procession of* **unemployed men** *shuffles in and joins the queue. Some are chattering, some smoking, some are silent, depressed and without energy.* **Mr Forrester**, *who is fighting faintness produced by hunger, finds himself at the front of the queue.*

MAN BEHIND *pushing him* You next, mate. Go on.

CLERK Next?

FATHER *bewildered by it all: this is not at all what he'd expected* Forrester. John Forrester.

CLERK Address?

FATHER Um . . . until the end of the week . . .

CLERK Permanent address?

FATHER No, not yet. We . . .

CLERK Date of birth?

FATHER 7th July, 1892.

CLERK What kind of work are you looking for, Mr Forrester?

FATHER Well, I thought possibly something in shipping. Insurance, perhaps. Or accountancy.

CLERK Professional qualifications?

FATHER No. I . . . um . . . No.

CLERK Previous experience?

FATHER No.

CLERK I'll put down clerk. Right, Mr Forrester, you're now registered for work as a clerk. Sign on Tuesdays and Thursdays. Next!

FATHER Um . . . excuse me . . . when do you think I might be found a position?

CLERK *looking up for the first time* Are you kidding me or what?

FATHER *reeling slightly as he struggles with faintness; he steadies himself on the edge of the table* The thing is, you see, I'm . . . well, the fact is I'm in rather an awkward situation.

MAN BEHIND Half bloomin' Liverpool is, mate.

CLERK You wait your turn.

MAN BEHIND It *is* my turn.

FATHER My wife's just had an operation and we've only recently moved up to Liverpool. Yesterday, in fact.

CLERK Chose the wrong place then, didn't you? Thirty per cent unemployment.

FATHER The difficulty is, look, I've got seven children to keep . . .

MAN BEHIND Blimey!

FATHER . . . and literally no money. Nothing.

CLERK Never contributed to Unemployment Insurance?

FATHER No.

CLERK No generous relations?

FATHER I'm afraid not.

MAN BEHIND One way ticket to the workhouse, mate.

CLERK You mind your own business. *To* **Father** Listen, I think the best thing you can do is to apply for parish relief.

FATHER Parish relief? Oh no, I couldn't possibly . . . How do I do that?

CLERK Go down the Public Assistance Offices. See what they say.

FATHER Thank you.

CLERK *as* **Father** *turns away and exits* Right. *Now* it's your turn. Name?

MAN BEHIND Ah, come on. You know me name.

SCENE FIVE

Helen *and the* **baby,** **Avril** *and* **Mrs Forrester** *are still in* *the room.* **Mrs Forrester** *is still lying on the sofa.* **Avril** *is playing listlessly.* **Helen** *sits in silence. The fire has gone out. They are very cold. The* **baby** *wails weakly.*

HELEN *narrating* All day Mother, Avril and I sat in silence in the icy room. Occasionally we fed the baby a little of the remaining milk. I'd have liked to get out . . . to get away from the smell . . . just to go for a walk. But I was afraid to ask. I was afraid to leave her. There was nothing to do. No books to read. No paper. Nothing to do but sit and think.

AVRIL When can we go home? I want to go home now.

MOTHER *dully* Be quiet Avril. For goodness' sake sit still.

AVRIL I'm hungry.

MOTHER *after a moment, almost to herself, with her eyes still closed* I could have married anyone. Anyone. Guy Warburton. Dickie de Souza. He was very keen. He's something very big in the Indian Civil Service. God knows how I could have been so stupid. Lieutenant Forrester. The thing was, he was in uniform, you see. I sometimes think that was half of it. More than half. I could never resist uniforms.

Mr Forrester *is letting himself in through the front door.*

HELEN *frightened by her mother's strange behaviour* Mummy, are you all right?

MOTHER *in a dull, muffled voice* For heaven's sake leave me alone.

AVRIL *rushing across the room* Daddy's coming! Daddy!

Mr Forrester *enters.* **Mrs Forrester** *struggles to sit up.*

MOTHER Well?

FATHER *freezing cold, huffing and rubbing his hands* Let me sit down first. Oh God . . .

MOTHER Have you found anything?

FATHER I'm registered for work.

MOTHER Is that all?

FATHER It's a start. They'll let me know as soon as a post becomes vacant. Celia, you should have seen it. All those unemployed men . . . queues of them stretching out onto the streets . . . queues of starving men . . . *After a* *moment* Anyway, the chap there sent me to the Public Assistance Committee.

MOTHER *horrified* The Guardians! They'll put us in the workhouse.

FATHER No, they were quite decent, actually. They try not to do that now. Apparently, I can claim forty-three shillings a week.

MOTHER Forty-three!

FATHER It ought to be more, but we don't qualify. They can only pay us whatever the minimum relief is in Surrey, because of having to reclaim it. And the Surrey rate isn't as high as the Liverpool rate.

MOTHER You mean, if we'd stayed where we were, which is what I always said we should do . . .

FATHER Well, I thought we'd probably do better coming to Liverpool. I still do. We need to make a new start.

MOTHER *furious* Oh, I should know better by now than to trust your judgement. Forty-three shillings! To keep nine of us! I spend more than that on a hat!

FATHER Perhaps if you'd spent rather less on hats . . .

MOTHER And you on books. Endless books. And wine. And entertaining hordes of friends. If you'd had the faintest idea how to manage financial affairs. If you'd even tried. Oh God, the mess you've got us into! *There is a silence buzzing with mutual accusation* Surely there's somebody left in Liverpool who remembers you. Or your father. I thought he was a Company Director . . . Chamber of Commerce or something. There must be somebody who'd give you a job on the strength of being 'old Forrester's son'.

HELEN *narrating* But it seems there wasn't. He wrote letter after letter.

FATHER *scribbling on a pad on his knee* Dear Sir, You may remember my father, William Forrester, who was, I believe, a friend and colleague of yours.

HELEN *narrating* Twice a week he went to sign on. He walked to the Unemployment Exchange.

CLERK'S VOICE Name?

FATHER *looking up, bewildered* Forrester. 7th July, 1892.

CLERK'S VOICE Sign here.

14

HELEN *narrating* Three miles there, three miles back. He wasn't as badly off as the dock labourers, he said. They had to sign on twice a day.

FATHER *still writing* Dear Sir, With reference to your advertisement in the Liverpool Echo of 11th January . . .

CLERK'S VOICE Next!

HELEN *narrating* The soles of his shoes began to wear out. His feet hurt him dreadfully in cold weather: fighting against the Red Army in Russia in 1919, he'd got severe frostbite. It still bothered him. I remember trying to rub the circulation back into his frozen feet.

SCENE SIX

*The **landlady** knocks at the door.*

LANDLADY Mr Forrester, are you in, love?

FATHER Come in.

LANDLADY *poking her head round the door* I just thought I'd better remind you, Mr Forrester. About the rooms. I've tenants coming in Monday morning. Out by half ten if that suits.

HELEN *narrating* My mother decided that this time *she* would find us somewhere to live.

MOTHER *she gets up from the sofa, starts to put on her coat and to tidy herself up* Well, I could hardly do worse, could I?

HELEN *narrating* For several days now she'd been practising trying to walk up and down stairs . . .

MOTHER To and from that stinking lavatory.

HELEN *narrating* But it wasn't easy for her. Her wound hadn't healed properly and the stitches were still in.

Mrs Forrester says goodbye to her husband and leaves the room. Mr Forrester takes Avril and sits down in a corner.

HELEN *narrating* Besides, she found the streets unnerving. Liverpool was like a foreign country to her.

Mrs Forrester, in coat and hat, passes two poorly-dressed women.

MRS FORRESTER *inclining her head graciously* Good morning.

1ST WOMAN *staring after her in amazement* Holy Mother!

2ND WOMAN Who the hell does she think she is? The Queen, or what?

Mrs Forrester knocks at a door. A woman opens it.

WOMAN Yeah?

MOTHER I've come about the sign in the window. Rooms to let.

WOMAN Just you, is it?

MOTHER And my husband, of course, yes. And the children.

WOMAN How many?

MOTHER Seven.

WOMAN This is a lodging house, love, not a bloomin' rabbit warren.

She slams the door shut.

MOTHER *furious* I beg your pardon! *She is gripped by a pain and staggers slightly; she says weakly* Oh God.

HELEN *narrating* From house to house. Up and down. 'Sorry, love.' 'No.' Doors slammed in her face.

Mrs Forrester struggles to get a grip on herself and knocks at another door. Mrs Foster opens it. She is very fat and has bronchitis. She seems a great deal nicer than she really is.

MRS FOSTER Yes, love?

MOTHER *still weakly* I've called about the accommodation to let.

MRS FOSTER You'd better come in.

MOTHER Thank you. My name's Mrs Forrester. *Coming over faint* I'm . . . Oh, dear . . . excuse me . . .

HELEN *narrating* That perpetual smell of boiled cabbage, rancid fat and dirt.

MOTHER Excuse me, just a minute . . . *But her knees buckle under her and she passes out.*

MRS FOSTER Oh Lord! *She struggles to kneel down and starts slapping Mrs Forrester's cheeks* Wake up . . . Come

16

on . . . you're all right, love. **Mrs Forrester** *starts coming to* It's all right, pet, you just had a little faint. That's all. *With difficulty* **Mrs Foster** *helps* **Mrs Forrester** *to her feet* You come and sit down. There we are. What you need is a nice hot cup of tea. Been real ill, haven't you, love?

MOTHER *collapsing gratefully onto the stairs, where she sits* Yes.

MRS FOSTER And you want a place for you and the kiddies, am I right? Well, I'll tell you what, love, I've got one room and an attic free at the top. Course I hadn't had it in mind to have kiddies up there again . . . the last family there was three kiddies . . . little horrors they were.

MOTHER I can assure you that my children are all very well behaved.

MRS FOSTER Oh, I'm sure they are, love, yes. Course, I would have to ask that bit extra for the kiddies, like. How many?

MOTHER Six. And the baby.

MRS FOSTER *sympathetically, as she sees the amount of rent she can ask growing ever higher* Ah, it's not easy, is it, love? Bit of a come-down in the world for you, this, eh? It's the noise, you see, with kiddies, isn't it? I have to consider me other tenants.

MOTHER These rooms you mentioned – are they furnished?

MRS FOSTER Oh yes, love. Furnished rooms. Course, you'll have your own little knick-knacks to make it a bit more homely, like.

MOTHER I wonder if I might see them.

MRS FOSTER If you can manage the stairs, love, you're welcome. This way . . . *And, panting and wheezing,* **Mrs Foster** *leads* **Mrs Forrester** *up the stairs* It's a long way up. Of course, since I've put on all this weight, me and me brother – we live together now . . . well, since Mother died anyway, we've moved into the downstairs rooms. More convenient. My brother was a professional pianist, you know. He was employed at the Empire Picture Palace. Oh yes. Mind out for the hole in the oil cloth, love. I don't think I mentioned, did I? I'm Mrs Foster.

HELEN *narrating* Sixty-four steps up from the coal cellar in the basement to the top attic. *And, as they climb, she*

17

counts in step with them, remembering how exhausting it
was . . . twenty-two . . . twenty-three . . . twenty-four . . .

MRS FOSTER *pausing to get her breath* That's the
bathroom. That's communal with the other tenants.

MOTHER Is there hot water?

MRS FOSTER Hot water? We don't supply hot water, love.
Carrying on I get a lot of trouble with silver fish in there.
And them beetle things. I'm always putting powder down,
but they don't seem that bothered, I find. *Leading* **Mrs
Forrester** *into the main area* This is your kitchen-living
room.

HELEN *narrating* A tiny grate. No stove. No water
supply. Three chairs. A broken sofa. A bed and a cupboard.

MRS FOSTER *opening the cupboard* There should be a
few bits of crockery in there. I did have some saucepans, but
them buggers I was telling you about did a flit with them.
And they did that and all. *Pointing to the settee* That's
why I'm forced to ask that bit extra when there's kiddies,
see, love.

MOTHER *weakly* Yes.

MRS FOSTER They've broken the window as well, look.
Never mind. You can put a bit of cardboard up to keep out
the draught. That's a very good bed that. Proper metal bed.

MOTHER Is there a mattress?

MRS FOSTER *ignoring her and leading her up to the area
which is the bedroom* And then upstairs again . . . Mind
your head, love . . . this is a nice cosy room.

HELEN *narrating* This was our room. The boys slept on
the double bed and my sisters shared the single one . . .

MRS FOSTER That one's propped up with bricks . . . lost
its leg somewhere. It's all right, though. Very firm. Try it.
Now, that door, that's another thing they had off, them
kiddies, but your husband can soon put it back on again,
can't he? It's a man's job that.

HELEN *narrating* That door was my bed. That's what I
slept on. My mattress was crumpled newspapers.

MRS FOSTER Now, you don't want to worry about the oil
cloth, love, it'll soon clean up. Nice bit of bedding and some
curtains at the windows . . . it'll look quite homely. You'll be
surprised.

MOTHER *helplessly* I really don't think, Mrs Foster . . .

MRS FOSTER *knowing perfectly well that there's no alternative* Oh, come on, love, you'll not find anywhere else willing to take on seven kiddies. Still, it's up to you. *A parting shot as she leaves* Twenty-seven shilling a week. In advance.

*Mrs Foster exits. Meanwhile the **family**, wearing their coats and carrying what few things they have to bring with them, enter the main room.*

SCENE SEVEN

HELEN *narrating* Five minutes after moving our new lodgings on the following Monday we began to appreciate some of the difficulties of living there.

*The **family** stare round the room.*

MOTHER *defensively* Well?

FATHER It's not . . . Twenty-seven shillings a week. It seems an awful lot. That's nearly twice as much as we paid at Brewer Street.

MOTHER *with growing hysteria* But this is a better neighbourhood, isn't it?

FATHER Is it?

MOTHER You can see it's a better neighbourhood. I mean, the square out there with the communal garden . . .

FATHER *hurriedly* Helen, go and get some coal. Get the fire lit. Make your mother a cup of tea.

HELEN I don't feel very well.

FATHER Where did I put the cigarettes? Come on, Helen, hurry up. We're all freezing. I'm going to have to do something about that window. *Suddenly the gas light goes out* Damn. Where's a penny for the meter?

*In the darkness he searches for money and, with **Alan's** help, inserts it.*

HELEN *narrating* The slot meter ate pennies at an alarming rate. We didn't know that these meters were installed by the landlords and set at the highest rate they thought they could squeeze out of their tenants. They had only to pay the gas company the amount calculated from reading the main house meter and then they pocketed the profit. A more worldly-wise person than my mother would have inserted a penny to see how long the gas lasted before accepting the tenancy.

FATHER   Where are the matches? Come on Helen, matches.

HELEN   *narrating*   But I had that kind of pain in my ear which I always had when tonsillitis was starting. My head throbbed. I could hardly hear what anyone said to me. I stumbled clumsily through the evening. I made tea and a little porridge for our supper, but I couldn't swallow anything. Avril ate all mine. I longed to go to bed.

SCENE EIGHT

*When the lights come up, it is early morning. The **children** are all in bed in the attic room, the three **boys** in the bed, the **girls** on the door which is supported by bricks. They are fully clothed and covered by their coats. In the main room **Mr and Mrs Forrester** are getting up. **Mr Forrester** sits on the side of the bed. The **baby** is crying.*

MOTHER   *calling up to the attic room*   Helen! Helen, time to get up. Will you feed and change Edward for me, there's a good girl? And put some water on for tea. We'll have to manage with just tea for breakfast: there isn't anything else.

FIONA   *who has woken up and is trying to rouse **Helen*** Mummy!

MOTHER   What?

FIONA   I think Helen's ill.

MOTHER   *on her way up to the attic bedroom*   What's the matter with her?

FIONA   And, Mummy, look, we've all got spots.

MOTHER   Who's got spots?

BRIAN   I've got spots. All over.

FIONA   Lift up your vest, Tony.

ALAN   Mine are itchy.

MOTHER   Well, it can't be chicken-pox. You've all had that. *Calling* John!

FATHER   *from the other room* Yes?

MOTHER   Come up here a minute. *To the* **children** And what's the matter with Helen?

HELEN   I think I've got tonsillitis.

FATHER   *coming into the room* What's going on?

MOTHER   Helen says she thinks she's got tonsillitis.

FATHER   You would. Just at the worst possible time. Open your mouth.

ALAN   Daddy, you're scratching. You've got spots too.

FATHER   Where? Oh no!

MOTHER   What is it?

FATHER   Bed bugs. Saw these when I was in the army.

MOTHER   *horrified* Bed bugs! *Growing hysterical* Oh no, oh no . . . no . . . I can't bear it . . . I can't . . . I can't bear it . . . *By now she is completely hysterical and screaming.*

FATHER   Celia . . . don't

FIONA   Mummy, stop it!

MOTHER   You must kill them . . . you must get rid of them.

FATHER   *helping her gently downstairs, as she is sobbing uncontrollably* Come on, Celia . . . come and lie down . . .

MOTHER   No!

FATHER   It'll be all right. It's not the end of the world.

MOTHER   It is! Oh God, it is. It's the end of my world.

He sits **Mrs Forrester** *gently down on the settee, where she collapses sobbing. The* **children**, *with the exception of* **Helen** *and* **Fiona**, *come downstairs.* **Helen** *stays in bed.*

FIONA   *narrating* Helen was ill for nearly two weeks. So I'll have to tell you what happened for a bit. It was horrible when she was ill. No one knew what to do. She was so ill she couldn't even talk to us. She just lay there. She moaned and whimpered, and she was burning hot but she kept shivering. She'd got tonsillitis and an abscess in her ear. We had to sleep on the floor. Daddy wanted to fetch a doctor, but there wasn't any money to pay him. And we hadn't got any aspirins either. There was no spare money. Mummy just lay on the settee all day, staring at nothing or crying.

21

MOTHER *through sobs* This isn't what I expected . . . I can't live like this . . . This isn't what I planned . . .

Mrs Foster comes wheezing up the stairs and stands in the doorway, her arms folded.

MRS FOSTER What do you mean, bugs? Are you accusing me of keeping a dirty house, Mr Forrester? If you've found any bugs, then all I can say is you must have brought them with you . . . *Going* And I'm getting complaints about the noise up here . . .

FIONA *narrating* When we were ill at home, Nanny used to change the sheets on our bed every day and bring us lemon barley to drink and little honey sandwiches. And we could listen to the wireless. I wish Mummy would stop crying.

FATHER *at door of attic bedroom* How is she?

HELEN *groggily* Is that you, Daddy?

FATHER Thank God.

HELEN Can I have something to drink? I'm thirsty.

The lights go out.

MOTHER John! Where are you? We need a penny for the gas.

SCENE NINE

When the lights come up, it is early morning. The **children** *are putting on their coats ready to go to school.* **Mrs Forrester** *is still lying on the settee.* **Helen** *is downstairs helping do up* **Brian's** *coat.* **Mr Forrester** *is trying to speak to his wife but seems unable to get through to her. He and the children are beginning to look shabby and pale.*

FATHER Celia, I've got to go. I've got to sign on this morning. Look, I'll drop the children off at school on the way. Then I'll just drop in at the library: see what jobs are advertised in *The Echo. There is no response. He can hardly bear it; he turns to* **Helen** Look, here's a shilling for the day's food. Milk for Edward, and then some potatoes, some rice . . . something filling for this evening. *He lowers his voice* Try and keep the little ones out of her way. Take them out. Get some fresh air.

22

HELEN *her voice still croaky from the tonsillitis* I can't find my coat, Daddy.

FATHER Your coat? No, that's right. We pawned it when you were ill.

HELEN Pawned my school coat?

FATHER Well, it doesn't matter. We'll redeem it as soon as we get next week's Assistance. Borrow your mother's.

He and the children leave the house. Out on the street, some **Liverpool girls** *are playing a skipping game. Two* **out-of-work men** *lean against a wall, smoking.*

GIRLS I am a Girl Guide dressed in blue,
These are the actions I must do.
Salute to the King, bow to the Queen
And turn my back to the people.
Pepper!

Mr Forrester and the **children** *pass them as they exit.* **Helen** *is putting on her mother's coat, which is much too long for her.*

HELEN *to her* **Mother** Will you be all right? *But there is no response* Come on, Avril. We're going shopping.

Helen picks up the **baby**, *takes* **Avril's** *hand and they leave the house and go into the street. The* **girls** *continue with their skipping game, but as soon as they see* **Helen** *they start jeering.*

GIRL 1 Eh, four-eyes, where are you going?

GIRL 2 Tell your mum your hem's come down.

HELEN *hurrying* **Avril** *past the girls* Don't look.

AVRIL I want to play.

HELEN *pulling at her* Come on!

A **Spanish woman** *is sitting on some steps. She calls to them.*

SPANISH WOMAN Hey! You . . . why you carry that baby? He too heavy, huh? You bring him here. *Helen brings* **Edward** *across to her and she croons over him* Que niño tan bonito. Aaah. You don't have pram?

HELEN No.

SPANISH WOMAN Is not your baby, no?

HELEN Yes, of course he's my baby. He's my brother.

SPANISH WOMAN   Ah! Brother! So. You are from number twelve?

HELEN   Yes.

SPANISH WOMAN   Listen. I have old pram. You want? My babies all grown. All big men now. So high. You wait.

She goes to look under the steps.

AVRIL   I'm cold. I want to play with those girls.

HELEN   Do you think she means a real pram?

*The **Spanish woman** emerges with a battered old pram.*

SPANISH WOMAN   Is a bit old. So what? You can tie it up with string.

HELEN   *overwhelmed*   Gosh. Thank you. Are you sure?

SPANISH WOMAN   You put baby in. See. He like that.

*She clucks and croons over him as **Helen** settles the **baby** into the pram.*

HELEN   Thank you very much.

SPANISH WOMAN   Any time you pass, you come see me. Yes?

HELEN   Yes, I will.

AVRIL   *as they exit*   Can I sit in it too?

HELEN   You're too big.

AVRIL   No, I'm not.

*The **Liverpool girls** finish their game and drift away. A ship's horn sounds in the distance. Some **sailors**, singing a little drunkenly, roll down the street. The **two men** part and wander off in different directions. There is the sound of a piano playing. **Helen** reappears, pushing the pram. She bumps and bangs it up the stairs to the room. The piano stops.*

MRS FOSTER'S BROTHER'S VOICE   I'm trying to practise! Who's that!

Helen pushes the pram into the main room.

MOTHER   *thoroughly alarmed by the noise*   What on earth . . . ?

HELEN   It's all right. It's only me.

MOTHER Take that thing . . . whatever it is . . . that filthy chariot thing out of here at once.

HELEN It's not a filthy chariot. It's for Edward. A foreign lady gave it to me. He likes it. Look. He's been asleep for ages. He can sleep in it at night as well. You'll be much more comfortable in bed without him.

MOTHER *listlessly* I suppose so.

HELEN It can be his bed as well as his pram. Shall I make you a cup of tea? *No response* Mummy? *No response* Shall I? *No response* Mummy?

Mr Forrester is coming upstairs. He looks exhausted. His shoes are stuffed with newspaper because the soles have gone. His shirt is dirty. His suit is crumpled and stained. He sits down and holds his head in his hands.

FATHER *after a moment, wearily* Any tea?

HELEN I'm just making a pot. *As she measures out the tea, she continues narrating* He was getting more and more exhausted. All day he tramped the streets of Liverpool looking for work. Nobody wanted him. He was too old, he had no experience, the way he spoke puzzled people. He was beginning to lose hope. And he was growing more and more worried about my mother. All day she sat there staring at nothing. It was over two months now since her operation and *still* the stitches hadn't been taken out.

FATHER *tentatively* Celia . . .

MOTHER No.

FATHER You must. What if they go septic? They're growing into the skin.

MOTHER We can't afford it. If you're so worried, you do it.

FATHER I can't do it!

MOTHER Why not? It's easy. You just cut them and pull. *Bitterly* Except that we haven't got any scissors. Not even a pair of scissors.

FATHER I asked a man in the queue at the Labour Exchange. He says there's a doctor round here . . . everyone knows him . . . who only charges what people can afford. *No response* It isn't just the stitches, Celia. You need to see a doctor. You're ill. I don't know how to help you. I only want you to be yourself again . . . to take an interest.

25

MOTHER To take an interest! In this? Why? What do you want me to do? Scrub floors with a bit of newspaper and cold water? Is that what you want? Try to wash out clothes that'll never get clean because we haven't got any soap, and never get dry because we haven't got a fire, and ought to be burnt anyway only we can't burn them because we haven't got anything else to wear? Why should I? Why should I take an interest in any of that? Oh, all right. All right. If you want me to go to a doctor, I will, but there's no doctor on earth will make me accept this.

FATHER I don't mean accept it. I mean . . .

MOTHER I will not give in. I will not admit it. You want me to be like you . . . accepting everything that happens . . . shuffling about getting shabbier and shabbier.

FATHER That's not true. I just want . . .

MOTHER I don't care what you want. All right, then. What's his address? This doctor. Where do I go?
To **Helen** Give me back my coat. I hope there aren't any vermin on it. They seem to be everywhere.

Helen pulls off the coat and Mrs Forrester inspects it carefully before putting it on.

FATHER I'll come with you.

MOTHER I can manage by myself. There's nothing wrong with me. I can manage.

She goes downstairs. As **Helen** *passes her* **Father** *a cup of tea, the lights fade.*

FATHER Damn!

SCENE TEN

When the lights come up, all the **children** *except* **Helen** *are in bed.* **Helen** *and* **Mr Forrester** *are in the main room.* **Mrs Forrester** *is climbing the stairs to the main room. She is singing cheerfully.* **Mr Forrester** *and* **Helen** *look at each other in surprise.* **Mrs Forrester** *comes in.*

MOTHER *gaily* Oh, it's freezing out there!

FATHER *confused by this extraordinary change of mood* What happened? Did he take the stitches out?

MOTHER Did he . . . ? Oh yes. Yes, he did.

26

FATHER How much did he charge?

MOTHER Nothing at all. From each according to his ability, to each according to his needs, that's what he said.

FATHER A Marxist.

MOTHER *horrified* You mean a communist? Oh no, I don't think so. He was a very sensitive and cultured young man. You've no idea what a pleasure it was to talk to somebody interesting for a change. He says I ought to try to find work. You mustn't leave yourself time to think, he said. Apparently it'll be easier for me to find work than it will be for you. I can't think why the idea didn't occur to me before.

FATHER What about Edward and Avril?

MOTHER What about Edward and Avril? Oh, I see. Well, Helen can look after them perfectly well, can't she? And give the others their tea when they get back from school.

HELEN But *I'm* going to school. You said as soon as Mummy was better I could go. You promised.

FATHER No. In fact, if I remember rightly, what I said was as soon as I've got a job you can go to school. And so you shall. A decent school.

HELEN But I want to go now. I haven't been to school for weeks. I'll forget everything, I'll get behind. Like Joan Harris with long division.

MOTHER Oh, for goodness' sake, Helen, don't be ridiculous.

HELEN But it's not fair!

FATHER If the doctor says your mother needs to do this, then she must do it, and we must all help in whatever way we can.

HELEN But I don't want to look after Avril and Edward. I want . . .

MOTHER 'I want, I want.'

HELEN *furious at being accused of selfishness* It's your job to look after them, not mine. That's your job.

MOTHER *coldly* I beg your pardon?

FATHER That's enough, Helen.

HELEN Well, it is her job.

FATHER I said that's enough. Go to bed. At once. And never let me hear you speaking to your mother like that again.

Furious, **Helen** *rushes up the stairs to the attic room.*

FATHER   And be quiet! You'll wake the children.

FIONA   *who has been sitting up in bed nervously listening to the row*   Why are you all shouting?

HELEN   *pulling off her shoes*   Anyway, it's illegal.

FIONA   What's illegal? What's happening?

HELEN   As soon as they find out I'm under fourteen they'll send an inspector round, and then I'll have to go to school.

FIONA   As soon as who finds out?

Helen *lies down and pulls part of Fiona's coat over her.*

HELEN   That's the trouble. There isn't anyone to find out. Nobody knows I exist.

FIONA   Do you mean at school? I could tell them, if you like. I could say I've got a sister who ought to be in the top class.

ALAN   If you do that, they'll prosecute Mummy and Daddy.

FIONA   What's prosecute?

ALAN   Put them in prison.

FIONA   *terrified*   I don't want Mummy and Daddy in prison.

HELEN   Move over.

ALAN   I don't know why you want to go to school, anyway. It's horrible. They keep saying 'Why do you talk with ollies in your mouth?' and hitting us. They say we smell.

HELEN   It's all right for you. You're a boy. Things'll just happen for you. And it's all right for you, Fiona, because you're pretty and you don't wear glasses. You'll get married. But I won't. And I want to be somebody. I don't want to be like Aunt Muriel, stuck at home looking after Granny all her life. I don't want to be that sort of trodden-on grownup. I want to be . . .   *She sniffs as if she might be crying*   Oh, go to sleep.

FIONA   Aren't you going to tell us a story tonight?

HELEN   *pulling the coat over her head*   I can't remember any.

SCENE ELEVEN

Downstairs, **Mr and Mrs Forrester** *are still sitting where they were.* **Mr Forrester** *crosses to join* **Mrs Forrester** *on the sofa.*

FATHER You mustn't let her upset you. Children say these things. She'll get over it.

MOTHER *peering at her face in her powder-compact mirror* No, actually, I was thinking I might make quite a good saleswoman. I used to be very good at church bazaars, didn't I?

FATHER It won't be as easy as a church bazaar, you know.

MOTHER Yes, I know. I don't expect it to be easy. I think that's what excites me. I do actually feel rather excited about it. And I do think I stand quite a good chance. For one thing I don't look as shabby as you do. I wish we could get your shoes mended. How do other people manage, John?

FATHER I don't know. I suppose if you're born to it . . .

MOTHER Yes.

FATHER There was a man in the queue at the Labour Exchange. He couldn't believe we wasted money on coal. He says you can keep a fire going for days on what you pick up on the streets. They've got hundreds of dodges, these men. Half of them illegal. Otherwise they'd starve. One man said to me the trick is to starve that little bit slower than the next man. Then there's one less in line for the next job that's going. He said I ought to write to my regiment.

MOTHER What for?

FATHER He says there are charitable grants for ex-servicemen.

MOTHER *hating the phrase* Charitable grants! *After a long silence* Are you hungry?

FATHER Yes.

MOTHER I can't believe how quickly you fall to the very bottom. I had no idea. All those people who think they're comfortably off . . . they think they're so safe. But once you start falling, it's as if you can't stop.

FATHER I keep dreaming about oranges. And lamb chops with mint sauce.

MOTHER I used to refuse food. I used to go to bridge parties and see all those buffet teas laid out . . . think of them . . . and the sight of so much food used to put me off.

FATHER You're still refusing food.

MOTHER I look hideous, don't I?

FATHER Of course you don't.

MOTHER I do. I saw myself in a mirror at the surgery. I'll put some lipstick on tomorrow. I've still got some. If only I could wash my hair properly. I think if I go to all the big department stores first . . .

FATHER *turning out the gas lights* You need to rest.

SCENE TWELVE

When the lights come up the rooms are empty except for **Helen,** **Avril** *and the* **baby.** **Helen** *is wrapping the baby up in his dirty blanket, ready to lay him in the pram.*

HELEN *narrating* In the morning they were both up and out early. My father gave me a shilling as usual to buy the day's food. *She pulls on a holey cardigan*

AVRIL Are we going out?

HELEN Yes.

AVRIL *peering into the pram* Is he ill? He doesn't cry any more, does he, like proper babies do.

HELEN I think it's because he's hungry. I suppose I'd better feed him before we go. I'll just run down and see if I can catch the milkman.

Helen sits Avril on the settee and then runs downstairs. Mrs Foster's brother is playing his piano, and the piano music continues in uninterrupted snatches until the end of Act I.

HELEN *narrating as she goes* It wasn't enough . . . the one pint of milk we could afford. Poor little Edward was slowly starving.

MRS FOSTER *poking her head round her door* Is that you, Helen Forrester? I've had complaints about that pram of yours on the stairs.

HELEN Yes, Mrs Foster. Sorry.

MRS FOSTER Can't you learn to walk down them stairs more ladylike?

HELEN I want to catch the milkman.

MRS FOSTER Too late. He's been.

She shuts her door. Helen sees two bottles of milk on the doorstep. She stares at them for a moment, looks up and down to see whether anyone is watching, and then pounds up the stairs again.

MRS FOSTER'S BROTHER'S VOICE Will you shut that racket on them stairs!

Helen takes two cracked mugs and fills one with water.

AVRIL What are you doing?

HELEN Ssh. Wait.

*Helen runs downstairs, taking care not to spill the water and looking furtively round. The coast is clear. Outside the front door, she hurriedly pours milk from each bottle into the empty mug, and then fills up the bottles with water. She shakes the bottle and replaces the cardboard tops. A **young policeman** has just turned the corner into the street. He stops and watches her. She is unaware of him. Finally, she hurries upstairs again. Her hands are trembling.*

AVRIL What were you doing?

HELEN Come on, quickly. We've got to go out.

*Helen puts the milk into a saucepan and covers it. Then she bumps the pram downstairs. Outside the **policeman** is examining the milk bottles. Then some **girls** run into the street and start playing. He moves back into the shadows.*

MRS FOSTER'S VOICE Helen Forrester, I've warned you.

Helen pushes the pram out of the front door. Once outside, she breathes a sigh of relief.

HELEN *narrating* Now I could buy the usual daily pint at the corner shop and Edward could have another two feeds.

*Helen pushes the pram out of sight. The **young policeman** follows her. The **girls** give up their game and wander off. **Two women** meet and greet each other. Another **woman** comes out of a shop with her groceries. **Helen** reappears with the pram and stops at the shop.*

HELEN Now, then, we want milk, don't we, and bread. Two pounds of potatoes. And what shall we have? A pennyworth of marg or a pennyworth of bacon pieces?

*The **young policeman**, who has been following her, is now right behind her.*

POLICEMAN   Nice baby you've got there.

HELEN   *jumping with fright*   Oh! Um . . . yes.

POLICEMAN   What's his name?

HELEN   *becoming increasingly nervous*   Edward.

POLICEMAN   *surprised by her accent*   Edward? That's a nice name. And what's yours?

HELEN   Helen. Helen Forrester.

POLICEMAN   And where's your Mam, Helen?

HELEN   She's out looking for work. So's Daddy.

POLICEMAN   I see. From somewhere down south, are you?

HELEN   Yes.

POLICEMAN   Any more brothers and sisters?

HELEN   They're all at school.

POLICEMAN   I see. Well, you'd better get on, love. You'll catch cold. You shouldn't be outside in just a cardigan this weather.

*Nervously, **Helen** goes into the shop. The **policeman** watches her go, and then walks away.*

HELEN   *narrating*   The following morning, an extraordinary thing happened. A pint of milk was delivered to the top of our staircase. The milkman insisted it was for Edward and was sent by a friend. 'What friend?' I said. 'We haven't got any friends any more.' But he wouldn't say. For two long years he climbed our stairs and deposited the daily pint of milk.

  Years later the shopkeeper told my mother about the young policeman who'd come into the shop asking questions about us, and who'd then apparently gone round to the dairy and ordered a daily pint of milk for Edward to be paid for out of his own meagre wages. I don't think there's any doubt that it saved Edward's life.

The piano music continues as the lights fade.

Act II
SCENE ONE

The street. **Mr Moritz** *is opening his pawnbroker's shop. Some* **women** *arrive with bundles of stuff to pawn and stop to gossip with one another.* **Helen** *enters, pushing the pram.* **Avril** *runs ahead.*

AVRIL   Where are we going today?

HELEN   *tired and cold*   I don't know. Just out.

AVRIL   There's Mr Moritz.

MORITZ   Look who it is! My little blue-eyed duck, my little Avril. You come to see your old Uncle Morry, yes? You got something for me today?

HELEN   Not today.

MORITZ   Nothing left to pawn, huh? So what can you do? Listen. I keep your coat out of sight. Round the back.

HELEN   Thank you.

MORITZ   Too much dust, too many moths in the shop. Let's see what I got in my pocket for my little sweetheart, eh? Nice big toffee.

HELEN   Say thank you, Avril.

MORITZ   Ah, she give me a big hug. Bye bye, my little duck.

Helen pushes the pram on.

AVRIL   Can we go there on our way home?

HELEN   *fiercely*   It *isn't* home. There was a garden at home. And an orchard with a swing. And a drawing room with bowls of flowers on all the little tables.

AVRIL   Can we?

HELEN   Don't you remember it?

AVRIL   Remember what?

HELEN   Home. You *must* remember it. *She makes a decision*   We'll go and find the Pier Head and watch the ferries going across. I'll show you where Birkenhead is. That's where you catch the train to Granny's house.

They go off. Meanwhile, an **old sailor** *starts fishing off the Pier Head. A ferry sounds its horn. We hear seagulls, the*

*sound of water and the distant sound of a warning bell. It's
very windy.* **Helen** *– pushing the pram – and* **Avril** *climb up
to the Pier Head. A* **man in uniform** *is directing people.*

MAN Next ferry in ten minutes. Come on. Queue over here,
please.

HELEN There you are, look . . . over there . . . and those
spires in the distance . . . that's Wallasey. There's fields over
there and the seaside.

AVRIL Are we going to see Granny?

HELEN We can't. Mummy and Daddy have quarrelled with
her. Avril! Come back! Keep away from the edge.

MAN Eh, come here, you! *He grabs* **Avril** *and hoists her to
safety*

HELEN Do as you're told, Avril.

MAN You want to be careful. You'll slip off the edge of the
landing stage, kid, and you'll be sucked under.

HELEN Excuse me, how much is it to go across on the
ferry?

MAN Twopence.

HELEN *dashed* Oh.

MAN Well, are you going or not?

HELEN No, thank you. *To* **Avril** Come on. *As they
go* One day I will, though. One day. Somehow or other.

SCENE TWO

Mr and Mrs Forrester *are climbing the stairs to the room.*

MOTHER Fifteen shillings a week they were paying for
that job! I was quite relieved not to get it. I said: 'Excuse
me, but can you tell me how you expect someone to live on
fifteen shillings a week and work such long hours?' That
shocked them. In the end, they chose some poor little
fourteen-year-old whom they can sack as soon as she's old
enough to be paid the adult rate. I was furious. Still, I
learned a lot. It was very interesting. Tomorrow, I'm going
to try that shop on the corner of William Brown Street.

HELEN *narrating* One day when they came home there was a visitor waiting for them. He had received my father's letter enquiring about charitable grants and was authorised, he said, to make them a payment of five pounds from regimental funds if conditions warranted it. If conditions warranted it! He took one look at us and the rooms and apologised for not being able to offer more. It seemed like a fortune to us. Five pounds. Alan and I were sent out to buy fish and chips as a treat.

Alan enters.

ALAN Hang on! Wait for me. What are we getting?

He joins **Helen** *at the fish shop. There is one* **woman** *in front of them and a* **woman** *and a* **man** *immediately behind. The* **woman** *in front, having been served, moves off.*

ASSISTANT Next.

WOMAN BEHIND It's you, love.

HELEN Oh . . . um . . . eight cod, chips and peas, please.

ASSISTANT Eight cod, chips, peas.

WOMAN You feeding the Merchant Navy, love?

MR GRIMSHAW *the man behind, pushing forward* Eh! You the kids from number twelve? Got a lot of money to throw about, haven't you?

ALAN A man came from Daddy's regiment and gave him five pounds.

HELEN *to* **Alan**, *trying to shut him up* Sssh!

MR GRIMSHAW A man from 'Daddy's' regiment? Oh, did he? Well, you can tell your 'Daddy' that Mr Grimshaw from the tobacconist's 'll be coming round to have a few words with him. I've got a little cigarette bill for your Daddy to settle.

WOMAN You be careful who you push around.

MR GRIMSAHW Don't you waste your sympathy on them, Missus. They're not worth it.

The **customers** *in the chip shop all start taking sides. The lights fade.*

SCENE THREE

When the lights come up, the **family** *is in the main room. They* *are in the middle of a row.* **Avril** *is crying.* **Tony** *is playing pretend cars on the floor.* **Brian** *sits listening, seriously frightened by the row.* **Fiona**, *wide-eyed with fear, cuddles her teddy bear.* **Mr Grimshaw**, *the tobacconist, is climbing the stairs.*

FATHER *shouting* Well, where do you think I got all those cigarettes from? Not on forty-three shillings a week. You smoked them as well. Why not? God, we must have something!

Mr Grimshaw *knocks on the door. Nobody moves for a few seconds.*

FATHER Open it, Helen.

Helen *opens the door.* **Mr Grimshaw** *comes in.*

MR GRIMSHAW I've come for me money.

FATHER Very well. How much do I owe you?

MR GRIMSHAW Thirty-seven and six.

MOTHER It can't be!

MR GRIMSHAW It bloody well is, Missus.

MOTHER Thirty-seven and six! That's ridiculous. Make him give you a proper bill.

FATHER Here. Here's your money. And now get out before I throw you out for swearing in front of a lady.

MR GRIMSHAW Don't you touch me, Mr Forrester. You lay one finger in on me and I'll have the law on you.

FATHER Out!

Mr Grimshaw *backs out and slams the door.*

MOTHER *calling after him* A receipt! *Furiously turning on* **Mr Forrester** You didn't ask for a bill. We've got no proof you owed him so much. And then you didn't even get a receipt from him.

FATHER That man insulted you. I will not . . .

MOTHER Oh, for heaven's sake! *After an angry silence* So, is there anything left out of that five pounds?

FATHER I had to pay Mrs Foster. I got behind with the rent.

MOTHER Give it to me.

FATHER What?

MOTHER   Give me what's left.

Mr Forrester takes a handful of loose change out of his pocket and hands it to her.

FATHER   *sheepishly*   I spent a bit on joining the library.

MOTHER   Joining the library! Oh, that's wonderful! Exactly what we need. Not food. Not coal. Not somewhere decent to live. Oh no. What we need is *books!*

FATHER   As a matter of fact I do need books.

HELEN   Can I take books out as well?

MOTHER   Be quiet. Is this all of it?

FATHER   Yes.

MOTHER   *efficiently counting the money out*   Right. One and nine for coal. Ten shillings. That'll redeem your coat, Helen. The rest I'll keep. Soap, we want. Needles, darning wool. Some aspirins.

ALAN   Can we have our fish and chips now?

FIONA   *in a small terrified voice*   I don't feel very hungry any more.

The lights fade. When they come up, the rooms are empty.

SCENE FOUR

Helen and Avril – with Edward in the pram – are in Mr Moritz's pawnshop. A couple of women are also in the shop. One has just handed her husband's suit over the counter.

MORITZ   Your husband's suit again, Mrs Kelly? So, his ship has sailed? Peace and quiet for a month or two, eh? What shall we say? I'll give you fifteen shillings for the lot.   *He gives her the money and a ticket*   Ah! See who it is! My little sweetheart. She should come and sit on the counter beside her uncle Morry. Upsadaisy.

The two women leave, counting out the fifteen shillings.

MORITZ   See you again, Mrs Kelly.

HELEN   I've come to redeem my coat.

MORITZ   Your coat! Excellent. Number two hundred and seventy-six. Good. That's very good. How much you got?

HELEN Ten shillings.

MORITZ So that will be nine shillings and ninepence.

HELEN No, it's ten shillings. Look . . .

MORITZ Who runs this shop? You or me? I say nine and ninepence, then nine and ninepence. All right? *He looks round the back for the coat.*

HELEN Thank you

MORITZ *from the back* Bit creased, this coat of yours. Not to worry. You can iron it.

He reappears with the creased coat.

HELEN I can't. I haven't got an iron.

MORITZ You need an iron? *He shouts into the back area* Joe! Go into the yard. Find a flat iron. Clean it up. You should go for a walk now. Come back later. I have an iron ready for you.

HELEN Thank you, Mr Moritz. That's very kind of you.

MORITZ Kind? Listen, so what is kind? Irons are threepence.

HELEN *laughing* Come on, Avril.

AVRIL I want to stay here.

HELEN We're going to the library and then we'll come back.

She pushes the pram away from the shop.

HELEN *narrating* Avril hated the library. But I loved it. I could have spent all day there, only these two would never stay quiet for more than ten minutes. Still, that was ten blissful minutes in a quiet, warm room, hovering by the radiator so as not to be seen in case somebody decided I was too grubby to be allowed in there. I could choose four books a week. Two fiction, two non-fiction. Four different worlds. Four ways of escaping. Four pieces of treasure. I loved that library. On the way back to pick up the flat iron . . .

*Some **boys** come barging past. One of them grabs at **Helen**'s glasses and knocks them to the ground. One pulls her hair. **Helen** is terrified. She panics in case her glasses break.*

BOYS Frogs' eyes! Ey, what do you want them for? Bean pole. Eh, rats' tails, never heard of a comb?

HELEN *narrating, as she picks up her glasses and puts them back on* I was terrified. After they'd gone, I shook so much I thought I was going to faint. We were passing Princess Park, so I wheeled the chariot in and sat down on the nearest bench and put my head between my knees.

*An elderly, immaculately dressed **gentleman**, with a silver-topped cane, is sitting on the bench reading. **Avril** plays a little distance away.*

OLD GENTLEMAN Are you better?

HELEN Yes, thank you. Come and sit down, Avril.

OLD GENTLEMAN No, let her play. She wants to play.

HELEN Won't she disturb you? Is that a Greek book you're reading?

OLD GENTLEMAN Greek? Oh no, no, no . . . not Greek. Arabic.

HELEN Arabic? Can you read Arabic?

OLD GENTLEMAN Oh yes. My mother was an Arab. So I know the language very well. One of my stronger languages. I can speak seven, you know, and read four more. Tell me where did you learn to speak English so beautifully?

HELEN *doubtfully* Do you think I do? Nanny always said I . . .

OLD GENTLEMAN Nanny?

HELEN Oh, well. No. We don't have a Nanny any more.

OLD GENTLEMAN I imagine not. You have a lot of books there. You like to read?

HELEN Yes, I've just . . .

OLD GENTLEMAN Good. That is very good. You go to school?

HELEN No. Not any more.

OLD GENTLEMAN No matter.

HELEN It does matter!

OLD GENTLEMAN Not in the least. The more time to read. Your day will come.

HELEN I don't think it will. I just get left to do everything. I don't think Mummy and Daddy care if I go to school or not.

OLD GENTLEMAN I see. Well, well. *After a pause* Imagine a boat . . .

HELEN Like a ferry boat, you mean?

OLD GENTLEMAN No, no . . . I mean a ship, an ocean liner. Imagine it: First Class . . . Second Class . . . Cabin Class . . . Everyone dancing, playing games, strolling on the decks . . . and hardly anyone there realises what a terrible thing has happened. Some of the passengers – yes, even some of the First-Class passengers – have fallen overboard. And a few of the dancers hear their calls for help, but they think: 'No, it is nothing to do with us. It is probably their own fault. It is somebody else's job to rescue them, not ours.' So the poor people thrash about in the water, and some are lucky and climb aboard the lifeboats. And others hang onto lifebelts and manage to keep their heads just above water. But many more can only grab at a slippery rock. The sea breaks over their heads. They scrabble desperately to get a hold. This is what has happened to your parents. So how can they reach out a hand to help you? But, you see, as soon as they are sitting safely on that rock, they will lean down and haul you up as well. *He gets up, ready to go* Well, I come here every sunny afternoon that I am free. You must come and see me again. Come and tell me what you've been reading.

HELEN *as he goes* Yes, I will. Thank you. Come on, Avril. Time to go home.

Helen pushes the pram out of the park.

SCENE FIVE

*In the street **children** gather in small groups to play games. **Fiona** is among a group who call to her to join them in a game of hop-scotch. She seems to be coughing rather a lot. **Alan**, **Brian** and **Tony** are with a gang of **lads** who are talking and messing about with a football etc. at the house, **Mrs Forrester** has just let herself in and is wearily climbing the stairs. **Mrs Foster** comes out from her room and calls upstairs.*

MRS FOSTER Who's that? Is that you, Mrs Forrester?

HELEN *narrating* You see. Even *I* was beginning to call it home.

MRS FOSTER I hope you realise that's two weeks' rent you owe me, Mrs Forrester. Two pound fourteen shilling.

HELEN *narrating* Summer in Liverpool. On hot days the alleyways stank. The children, on holiday from school, played in the streets all day with their new friends. They forgot that there had ever been any other kind of life. Now when I told them stories about our real home, they looked puzzled and a bit bored as if they didn't really understand the point of the story.

MRS FOSTER That husband of yours hasn't paid me since the beginning of August!

HELEN *narrating* The leaves in the park grew dusty. My coat went back to Mr Moritz. My thirteenth birthday came and went.

MOTHER *calling down the stairs* You'll have to speak to *him* then, won't you?

MRS FOSTER Two pound fourteen shilling by Friday or I shall have to ask you to vacate the premises.

Mrs Foster returns to her room. **Mrs Forrester** *lies back on the sofa with her eyes closed. Slowly the* **children** *begin to disperse.* **Fiona**, **Alan**, **Brian** *and* **Tony** *straggle up the stairs.*

HELEN *narrating* Winter again. How to face a second winter? We were anaemic and prone to infections. We had no energy. Fiona seemed to have a permanent cough. Our skin flaked and broke out in sores. Bites turned septic. 'Dirty little ragamuffins', the commissionaire shouted when he turned Avril and me out of the Museum. And yet in some ways we were tougher. Nothing seemed as shocking or as terrible as it had done the first winter. Although there was the problem of our shoes. When mine fell to pieces I was lucky enough to find a pair of plimsolls on a rubbish heap. They more or less fitted. But my father had nothing to wear on his feet.

SCENE SIX

Mr Forrester *shuffles across in shoes held together with paper and string to where the* **Public Assistance Officer** *has set up his table. A* **charity worker** *sets up a table on the other side of the stage.*

PUBLIC ASSISTANCE OFFICER Next!

FATHER It's about boots. I need a pair of boots. I wondered if it would be possible to get some sort of allowance . . .

PUBLIC ASSISTANCE OFFICER We don't give money for that sort of thing. We can give you a pair out of stores, but they'd be stamped 'PROPERTY OF THE PUBLIC ASSISTANCE COMMITTEE'.

FATHER *gratefully* I don't care what they're stamped with.

PUBLIC ASSISTANCE OFFICER Stops people pawning them. Ah, but hang on a minute. You're not eligible, are you? You don't come under Liverpool. I tell you what . . . you could try one of the charity agencies.

Mr Forrester crosses the stage to the other desk.

FATHER Good morning. I need a pair of boots. The Public Assistance suggested I try . . .

CHARITY WORKER Are you drawing Public Assistance?

FATHER Yes, but . . .

CHARITY WORKER Then I'm afraid we can't help you. You'll have to go back and speak to them about it. It's their responsibility.

FATHER Yes, but you see I'm not eligible. I don't . . .

CHARITY WORKER I'm sorry. We have to stick to the regulations.

FATHER *hopelessly* Yes. Yes, I see. Thank you.

SCENE SEVEN

Mr Forrester shuffles back, lets himself in to Mrs Foster's house and climbs the stairs. During the previous scene two large boxes have been left in the hall.

MOTHER *the moment he comes through the door, very excited* There you are! Where on earth have you been? Listen! Listen to this! I . . . have got a job! Selling wireless sets on commission.

FATHER A job? *He collapses shakily into a chair.*

Mrs Foster has come out of her room. She notices the boxes, and examines them to see to whom they belong.

MRS FOSTER *calling upstairs* Mrs Forrester! What are these boxes doing in my front hall?

MOTHER Oh damn. *Calling down* I am just on my way to move them, Mrs Foster. Give me a hand, Alan. *She goes downstairs, followed by* **Alan**.

MRS FOSTER Littering the place up where people want to come in and out.

MOTHER *coldly* I'd be obliged if you didn't touch anything, Mrs Foster. It's a wireless set. A demonstration model. I shall be selling them from now on.

MRS FOSTER Hmm! You'd do better business flogging a dead horse in this area.

MOTHER I've no intention of even trying this area. I can't think of anyone round here likely to appreciate good music.

MRS FOSTER *bristling with fury* My brother, may I remind you, Mrs Forrester, was one of the finest pianists they ever employed at the Empire Picture Palace.

MOTHER *icily gracious* I'm sure he was, Mrs Foster. Nevertheless, I think Anfield . . . Walton . . . those are the kind of places where I shall be doing most business. As a matter of fact I'm taking this model over to Anfield this evening. A young woman wants her husband to see a demonstration model before they commit themselves. *She struggles to pick up one of the boxes.*

MRS FOSTER *with satisfaction* That's the acid battery you're tipping over, Mrs Forrester. *She bustles back into her room* You'll not carry that lot over to Anfield.

MOTHER *rubbing her leg, almost in tears* It's burnt me.

ALAN She's right, though. About carrying it over to Anfield.

At this moment, **Helen** *and* **Avril** *come in with the pram.*

MOTHER *irritably* For heaven's sake, Helen, move out of the way with that thing. You can see there's no room.

ALAN We could use that! We could use the chariot!

The lights fade.

SCENE EIGHT

*The lights do not come fully up again, but we can just see **Mr Forrester**, **Helen** and all the **children** lurking in the shadow with the chariot. **Helen** is holding the **baby**. Again, she has to wear a holey cardigan instead of a coat. They speak in low voices.*

FATHER   That's a policeman over there. Look. By the shops. We'd better get a move on. Stand still for five minutes in an area like this and they nab you for vagrancy.

ALAN   There's Mummy.

AVRIL   I want to go home.

FATHER   Celia! Over here!

Mrs Forrester joins them. She is transfigured with excitement.

MOTHER   I sold it! John, I did it! I sold that very one. They were so impressed, they wanted the demonstration model. I *knew* I could do it.

FATHER   Celia, that's splendid. Well done.

MOTHER   *in a daze of pleasure*   And they gave me a cup of tea, and a slice of sponge cake. With jam in.

FATHER   How much commission will you get?

MOTHER   Thirty shillings! Think of it. Thirty shillings for one day's work.

FATHER   The trouble is, though, I'm honour bound to tell the Public Assistance Committee . . .

MOTHER   Tell the Public Assistance! Are you mad?

FATHER   I'll have to. It's dishonest not to. And suppose they found out?

MOTHER   Damn the Public Assistance Committee. Why should I care about them? You listen to me, John Forrester, the only obligation we have is to ourselves. To survive. This is my money. I earned it. It's nothing to do with them. And you need boots. Fiona needs cough medicine. Anyway, think of it! If I sell one wireless set a day with Sundays off . . . that'll be . . . what? Nine pounds a week. And to hell with Public Assistance.

FATHER Sssh. That policeman's still there. We'd better move on.

MOTHER *as they go off* Better put Edward back in the chariot now, Helen. It was a good idea, that. I'll be needing it again quite often.

HELEN *narrating* She didn't. She never managed to sell another. My father got his boots and Fiona – for all the good it did her – got her cough medicine. And that was that. After a couple of weeks she got the sack. She said the trouble was it was too near Christmas: people didn't have the money for things like wireless sets.

The lights fade.

SCENE NINE

When the lights come up the **family** *are sitting gloomily in the main room.* **Brian** *and* **Tony** *are squabbling.*

HELEN *narrating* Christmas Eve. We sat staring at a fire made up of street scavengings . . . an old shoe, some rags, a cardboard box. After an hour it went out.

Mrs Foster comes out of her room with a parcel and starts wheezing her way upstairs.

MOTHER *on the edge of hysteria* I can't stand sitting around in here. I'm going to bed.

FATHER Celia, it's Christmas Eve!

MOTHER I don't care what it is.

Mrs Foster, gasping and breathless, knocks at the door

MRS FOSTER Mr Forrester! Are you in, Mr Forrester?

MOTHER *nastily* Have you paid the rent this week?

MRS FOSTER Parcel for you.

Mr Forrester opens the door.

FATHER A parcel? Who on earth is sending us a parcel? Come in, Mrs Foster.

MRS FOSTER It's one of them Relief Charity Parcels. For the unemployed. It came this afternoon, only there was nobody in.

MOTHER Thank you very much, Mrs Foster. That will be all.

MRS FOSTER Aren't you going to open it, then? You better had, love. There's a turkey in there. I know that for a fact. You don't want it to go off.

HELEN A turkey!

*The **children** excitedly start opening the parcel, exclaiming over everything they find.*

MRS FOSTER There's always a turkey in them parcels. Or a chicken. And a Christmas pudding.

ALAN There's some sweets!

HELEN And oranges. Look. Oranges!

MOTHER *beginning to laugh hysterically* A turkey! A turkey!

*Her laughter frightens the **children**, and silences them.*

FATHER *anxiously* Celia . . .

MRS FOSTER Is she all right?

FATHER Celia, please . . .

MOTHER Tell me . . . tell me, Mrs Foster . . . no, don't scuttle away downstairs . . . tell me this: since you've failed to provide your so-called 'furnished' rooms with any kind of stove, and since my husband has failed to provide his family with any coal over the festive season, do please tell me how you advise us to cook this turkey? Do we tear it apart in our hands and eat it raw? *Laughing hysterically again* A turkey! They send us a turkey.

FATHER Oh, Celia, you mustn't . . .

MOTHER Don't touch me!

MRS FOSTER She's overwrought. I said to my brother when she first came here, I said that's a very finely bred, very highly strung woman. *Awkwardly* I tell you what, Mr Forrester, love, you bring it downstairs. I've got my oven all nicely heating up for our turkey tomorrow, so I might as well put it to good use. Have you got any potatoes?

*The lights fade. The **family** groan.*

MOTHER That's it! That's the last straw.

FATHER No, it's all right. It's all right. We've got a candle. Where are the matches?

*After a moment a match is struck and a candle lit. **Helen** is
holding a candle. We hear behind her voice the sounds of the
family laughing and eating together.*

HELEN *narrating* The taste of that turkey . . . eaten in
the early hours of Christmas morning by candlelight
because the gas had run out. Crisp fatty skin . . . soft white
meat . . . a huge basin of dripping . . . roast potatoes . . .
oranges . . . toffees . . . *Slowly, the **family** fall silent* And
so Christmas came and went. We'd been a whole year in
Liverpool. I was thirteen and a half. My mother got a
temporary job demonstrating babies' baths in a department
store. She was very good at it. She was only on commission,
of course, so she didn't earn very much, but my father could
see how much better she was when she was working, and he
relaxed a little.

She blows out the candle

Act III
SCENE ONE

*Prince's Park. The first bright day of summer. The **old
gentleman** is sitting on the park bench, and **Helen** is
standing there talking to him.*

OLD GENTLEMAN Ah, yes. I remember you. My very
interesting little friend who likes to read.

HELEN I came to ask you something. You know you said
school didn't matter? What I'm wondering is, how am I ever
going to get a job if I haven't got any qualifications?

OLD GENTLEMAN Oh, qualifications. What are they?
Bits of paper. You can pick up qualifications at night school
any time.

HELEN *Night* school? Do they have school at night?

OLD GENTLEMAN Of course they have school at night.
All over Liverpool.

HELEN I didn't know that. Nobody told me.

OLD GENTLEMAN Now where are you going?

47

HELEN   I'll come and see you again.

OLD GENTLEMAN   I shall want to know all about the books you've read.

SCENE TWO

*Helen is running through the door of the house and up the stairs. She flings herself through the door. **Mr and Mrs Forrester** look up in surprise.*

HELEN   Daddy?

FATHER   What?

HELEN   You never told me about night school.

FATHER   What are you talking about?

HELEN   You never told me I could go to night school.

MOTHER   Because you can't. The first thing they'd want to know would be your age. And then they'd start checking.

FATHER   I thought we'd explained all this.

HELEN   But I've got to go to night school. I've got to.

FATHER   What's this obsession of yours with education? That's the sort of thing Alan should be worrying about, not you. As soon as I get a job . . .

HELEN   Oh, Daddy . . .

FATHER   No, I made you a promise. I haven't forgotten. As soon as I've got a job you'll be going to a really good school. Maybe a finishing school. Somewhere like that. But until things are sorted out, your mother needs you to look after the children.

HELEN   I'm sick of looking after the children. Why do I have to do everything?

FATHER   That's enough. I won't have you upsetting your mother.

HELEN   . . . And then stupid lies about finishing school. I'm not going to a finishing school.

MOTHER   Don't you dare speak to your father like that. Go to your room.

HELEN   *storming out of the door and downstairs* I haven't got a room. I haven't got anything.

FATHER Should I go after her, do you think?

MOTHER Leave her alone. Let her cool down. She'll get over it.

HELEN *standing outside the door to the house. Narrating* I didn't get over it. And only a week later, their hands were forced.

SCENE THREE

*A **teacher** approaches the front door. She is supporting a very ill-looking **Fiona.***

HELEN *alarmed* Fiona! What is it? What's the matter?

TEACHER She's not well at all. You know her, do you?

HELEN She's my sister.

TEACHER Yes, of course. The accent. Well, I'm afraid she's been coughing very badly all morning and at dinner time she fainted in the playground.

HELEN I'll take her upstairs.

TEACHER *looking round* This is where you live, is it?

HELEN Yes.

TEACHER I didn't realise Fiona had a big sister. We haven't seen you at school, have we? *Helen doesn't know what to say* How old are you, dear?

HELEN *after struggling between loyalty to her parents and loyalty to herself* Thirteen and three-quarters.

TEACHER I see.

*A bell rings. **Children** stream into the playground to start playing, and **Helen** stands where she is, watching them.*

FATHER *looking down from upstairs* Of all the underhand, ungrateful children . . .

MOTHER Suppose they prosecute? This is impossible. Quite impossible. I suppose you think jobs grow on trees.

FATHER I don't know how you could bring yourself to do it, Helen. You know how things are. You know your mother needs to work.

HELEN *narrating* Eight weeks of being a schoolgirl again. Every day I had to go home and face two outraged parents, but it didn't matter. I hardly cared about anything except the pleasure of being praised again. Being able to play hopscotch. Or tag. Radiators. Pencils and paper. To be thirteen again. Not to have to worry about anything. *She runs into the rope of a girls' skipping game* To play in the playground. *She does a couple of skips and then runs out again.*

ART TEACHER Helen Forrester?

HELEN Yes, sir.

ART TEACHER Ah, there you are. Good. I just thought I'd let you know that I've put your name down for a scholarship to the City Art School.

HELEN *narrating* The City Art School. A scholarship! I could hardly breathe for excitement. *She runs back into the skipping game again* All I had to do was to send in all the drawings I'd done . . . I was always good at art . . . and do an easy exam paper.

Helen runs out of the skipping game and back to the door of the house. The bell rings. The children go back into school. Helen stays where she is.

HELEN *narrating* My fourteenth birthday, and I was back where I started. *She opens the door and goes in, closing it behind her* The holiday was over. Pushing Edward's pram to and from the shops . . . the park . . . scavenging the streets for something to burn . . . cooking the evening meal . . . trying to keep our rooms clean. Except now there was always the thought of the scholarship, and I pinned all my hopes on it. Every day I hovered in the hall waiting for news.

Mrs Foster comes out of her room and almost bumps into Helen.

MRS FOSTER Are you coming in or going out, Helen Forrester? I'm sick of tripping over you wherever I go.

HELEN I'm waiting for the post, Mrs Foster.

MRS FOSTER The post's been.

HELEN Oh.

MRS FOSTER And I may as well mention it to you, Helen. You can tell your Mam. I'm getting fed up with these complaints.

HELEN About the chariot again? I'm sorry. I do try to be quiet.

50

MRS FOSTER It's your sister Fiona I'm talking about. That cough of hers. Mrs Hicks on the second floor says it keeps her awake all night. You tell your Mam to take her to the doctor. I don't want nothing infectious in this house.

SCENE FOUR

*Mrs Foster shuts her door and the lights fade. When the lights come up again, a **crowd** has collected both inside and outside the house. Two **ambulancemen** are coming down the stairs. One is carrying **Fiona**.*

AMBULANCEMAN Come on. Clear the way. Mind out the way, Missus. Which one of you's coming in the ambulance with her? Mum or Dad?

MOTHER I am. I will. You stay here, John. Look after the children. Helen and I will go.

*Some of the **crowd** follows the **ambulancemen** out of sight. The rest disperse, chattering excitedly. **Helen** and **Mrs Forrester** reappear and settle nervously on a bench.*

HELEN *looking round the huge hall in which they are sitting; narrating* The Children's Sanatorium. A huge place. A place everyone dreaded. The TB Hospital.

*They sit in silence for a moment, then a **nurse** enters briskly. She is holding a brown paper parcel as if it might bite her.*

NURSE Mrs Forrester?

MOTHER *leaping to her feet* Can I see her?

NURSE Are you Mrs Forrester?

MOTHER Yes.

NURSE We've just given her a disinfectant bath. These are her clothes. I suggest you burn them. I suppose you realise they're verminous?

MOTHER Can I please see my daughter?

NURSE Certainly not. The doctor hasn't seen her yet.

MOTHER Then I'll wait until I can see her.

NURSE *as she walks away* I imagine there'll be questions asked. Goodness knows how anyone could let a child get into that state . . .

Mrs Forrester sits down again. There is another pause.

MOTHER Monday's child is fair of face . . .

HELEN *confused* What?

MOTHER Monday's child is fair of face. Fiona was born on a Monday. She was always so pretty . . . You were born on a Saturday, of course. Saturday's child works hard for a living.

HELEN *narrating* We sat there for hours. It got dark outside.

*They sit for a minute. Then the **nurse** reappears.*

MOTHER Excuse me . . .

NURSE What are you doing here? It's half past two in the morning, Mrs Forrester.

MOTHER I said I would wait.

NURSE Well, there's nobody here. The doctor's gone home.

MOTHER Gone home?

NURSE Of course he's gone home. Hours ago. Fiona's asleep. She's not to be disturbed. She's a very sick little girl.

MOTHER What did he say?

NURSE They'll take X-rays of her chest tomorrow. He did say, though, that it looked like pleurisy.

Mrs Forrester is patently relieved: she was terrified that it might be TB. Pleurisy, serious though it was, seemed almost like a reprieve.

NURSE You'd better go home, Mrs Forrester. You really can't stay here.

The lights fade.

SCENE FIVE

*When the lights come up again, **Helen** and **Mrs Forrester** are climbing the stairs and going into the room.*

FATHER *lifting his head from his hands* Celia?
MOTHER Yes.
FATHER Thank God. What's happened?

MOTHER I'm sorry. We waited to see the doctor, but he'd gone.

FATHER Did they tell you anything?

MOTHER They think it's pleurisy.

FATHER Pleurisy? Are you sure?

He begins to weep silently in his relief. **Mrs Forrester** *kneels to comfort him.*

MOTHER They're going to take X-rays tomorrow.

FATHER Not TB?

MOTHER They don't seem to think so, no.

FATHER Oh, thank God . . .

MOTHER Oh, John, don't . . . please don't . . .

Mrs Forrester continues to hold and comfort her husband while Helen narrates.

HELEN *narrating* And so I forgot all about the scholarship. Nothing had come in the post. No one had said anything. And we were all too bothered about Fiona's illness to think about anything else. It took a month for the pleurisy to drain, and it was weeks after that before she was allowed home. They fed her on porridge and plain steamed fish and boiled puddings.

The **nurse** *and the* **Public Assistance clerk** *enter and stand at the far side of the stage.*

NURSE Relatives are required to supplement the basic diet. Suggested supplements are milk, butter, margarine, jam, fruit and sugar.

HELEN *narrating* Goodness knows how we were supposed to afford it. We couldn't even afford the tram fare out to the sanatorium.

CLERK Name?

FATHER *still up in the room, lifting his head automatically to answer* Forrester, John.

CLERK Thirty-five shillings. That's an eight shilling a week cut while your daughter's in the sanatorium.

MOTHER *furious, now trying to shake some of her own anger into her husband* Damn them! Oh, please, John, you mustn't let them hurt you. Don't let them humiliate you. They're nothing. Listen, I've found a way to get the tram fare out to the sanatorium. Every telephone box you pass, you press Button B. Helen and I got fourpence yesterday. *But there is no response* Fight them, John. You've got to. Don't let anybody see you're beaten.

*The **nurse** and the **clerk** have gone.*

SCENE SIX

HELEN *narrating* September came. The children went back to school. Avril started in the infants class. Fiona grew fatter and stronger even though we couldn't supplement her diet. What they gave her at the sanatorium was a great deal better than anything she ever got at home. And as for Edward and me . . . we went on as before.

***Helen** starts bumping the pram downstairs. In the main room **Mr and Mrs Forrester** are stting on either side of the grate. **Alan**, on his way home from school, meets **Helen** on the stairs.*

ALAN *excited* Helen, listen . . .

HELEN *irritably* What? Get out of the way.

ALAN The headmaster came into our class today.

HELEN *trying to manoeuvre the pram past him* Oh, Alan! Either come up or go down.

ALAN Yes, but listen. He said: 'How's your sister enjoying life at the City Art School, Alan?'

HELEN *suddenly alert* What?

ALAN I didn't know what to say.

HELEN It's a mistake. It must be. Tell me again what he said.

ALAN He said: 'How's your clever sister Helen enjoying life at the City Art School?' I didn't know what he meant. What did he mean?

HELEN Then I *did* win it! I did win. Here. You take him.

*She abandons the pram. **Alan** is left to get it downstairs.*

ALAN What do I do with him . . . ?

*But **Helen** is running back up, muttering furiously to herself.*

HELEN I did win it. I won. I won.

She flings open the door.

FATHER *looking up from his book* I have asked you to be quieter on those stairs. *He sees her face* What's the matter with you? Where's Edward?

HELEN *controlling herself carefully* I came to ask you if you ever heard anything about that art scholarship I sat for?

FATHER Art scholarship?

HELEN Yes. I'm sure you remember.

FATHER Oh yes. Yes, we did hear something about that. Unfortunately, though, it couldn't be awarded to you.

HELEN So I did win?

FATHER Yes, you did. The problem was, of course – the same old problem – you weren't born in Liverpool. That disqualified you.

HELEN I see. So why didn't you tell me?

MOTHER It all happened when Fiona was so ill. We thought you'd be upset.

HELEN I ought to have been told.

MOTHER Your father thought . . .

HELEN You should have told me.

FATHER Be reasonable, Helen. What was the point? They weren't going to allow you to take up the scholarship, so . . .

HELEN *Who* wasn't? *Who* wasn't going to allow me? *She looks from one to the other, but they both avoid her eyes* It seems very odd, doesn't it? The school knew where I was born. They had to put the place and date of birth on the entry form. And surely they knew the rules. So why did they put me in for it?

MOTHER *changing the subject deliberately* What a terrible racket they're making over the road. I suppose there must be a ship in. The place is reeling with sailors. Helen, have you left Edward in the hall?

Helen turns on her heel and runs downstairs. She takes the pram from Alan without speaking and goes out into the street.

ALAN What's the matter? What's going on?

The lights fade; as they fade Helen narrates.

HELEN In the end I decided to believe them. What else could I do? I wasn't brave enough to live with the alternative explanation: that they'd deliberately hidden that letter from me so that I couldn't go to the City Art School. Because it would be too inconvenient for them . . . because they needed me to look after the children. No. They were my parents. They must have wanted what was best for me. Of course they were telling the truth.

SCENE SEVEN

*The lights have completely faded now. When the lights come up again, **Mrs Forrester** and the **children** are in the room. **Mr Forrester** and **Brian** are out in the street. Other **shoppers** walk to and fro. A plain-clothes **policeman** has noticed **Mr Forrester**.*

HELEN *narrating* And then one day, something extraordinary happened. My father was wandering about in town. He and Brian were looking at the tailors' shops in North John Street, when he noticed a man watching him. He was always afraid of being arrested for vagrancy, and there was something suspicious about the way this man was staring at him. And something even more suspicious about his highly-polished boots. Possibly a plain-clothes policeman.

MOTHER Helen!

HELEN I'm coming.

*Helen goes in, leaving the pram in the hall and goes up the stairs. Meanwhile **Mr Forrester** has become very aware of the man watching him. He takes **Brian**'s hand.*

FATHER Come on. We'd better get out of here. *They start to walk away, weaving between the people in the crowd.*

MAN Hey! hang on a minute!

FATHER Go on, Brian! Quick. Run. As fast as you can.

*Brian streaks off. **Mr Forrester** starts to run too, but he's weak from lack of food, his boots are falling apart and he keeps bumping into people.*

MAN Hey! You! Stop!

*The plain-clothes **policeman** catches up with **Mr Forrester** and grabs his arm.*

MAN Hang on a minute, sir.

56

FATHER *gasping for breath* I am not a tramp . . . I know I look . . .

MAN That's all right, sir. You just get your breath back.

FATHER Are you arresting me for vagrancy? I swear to you . . .

MAN I'm not arresting you for anything.. It was simply that I noticed your tie.

Brian has run home, dashed up the stairs and is telling Mrs Forrester and Helen what has happened. We only hear what is going on in the street, but we do see the family's consternation.

FATHER My tie?

MAN Where did you get it?

FATHER It's mine. It's my old school tie. All Saints.

MAN You were at All Saints?

FATHER I know it may seem unlikely, but yes, I . . .

MAN What years?

FATHER Uh . . . between 1904 . . . no, 1905 and 1910.

MAN Ah well, now, I left in 1906.

FATHER You were there too?

MAN I was indeed.

FATHER So you'll remember old Spudgy Holland?

MAN Of course I remember old Spudgy Holland. Good Lord. Look, let me introduce myself. Peter Molloy. Detective Inspector.

FATHER John Forrester.

MAN John Forrester? The little lad who got knocked out by a cricket ball?

FATHER That's right. *He staggers and almost faints.*

MAN Good God, man, you need a solid meal inside you. I've got a car round the corner. Come on. *He half supports Mr Forrester as they go off.* So were you there when old Spudgy Holland fell into the river . . . ?

In the room, Mrs Forrester is growing anxious. She is pacing to and fro.

MOTHER If we only knew which police station he was being held at.

HELEN   If they keep him overnight, they'll have to come and tell us what they're charging him with, won't they?

MOTHER   *to Brian*   Tell me again exactly what happened.

Brian opens his mouth to speak when they hear the sound of a car drawing up.

MOTHER   Ssh!

*We hear **Mr Forrester**'s voice saying goodnight, thank you etc. Then he lets himself in through the front door and goes upstairs.*

MOTHER   It's him! It's your father! Thank God. John!

FATHER   *bursting in, full of excitement*   Celia, you will never believe what's just happened to me.

HELEN   *narrating*   They talked for hours. It seemed like a miracle. Peter Molloy, the Detective Inspector, was horrified to hear what had happened to my father. He took him back to the police station for a good square meal, and he promised to use his influence with the City Council to get my father some sort of job. He also arranged to get in touch with the executors of the All Saints Benevolent Fund. He said the fund would probably give my father a grant to buy some decent clothes for his interview.

MOTHER   You mean the school Benevolent Fund!   *She laughs*   Good Lord, the amount of money you used to contribute to that fund. Every year it was the same: 'Oh Lord, Celia, I've forgotten that damned Benevolent thing again. Send them a cheque, will you?   *Suddenly serious*   Is it true, John? Really true?

FATHER   *smiling at her*   Really true.

MOTHER   So it's over. It's all over. It's going to be all right.

*Mr and Mrs Forrester hug each other and the **children** dance about with excitement. The lights begin to fade. **Helen** detaches herself from the celebration.*

HELEN   *narrating*   But it wasn't all right. Of course it wasn't. 'As soon as I get a job,' he said. 'I've made you a promise.' And he did get a job . . . all cleaned up in his new suit . . . a temporary clerk at City Hall. 'Temporary' meant nothing. All the posts were temporary. It saved the impoverished City from having to pay pensions. Never mind the pension, the wages were only a few shillings a week more than we'd been getting on Public Assistance, and now there were tram fares to pay for and some kind of position to keep up.

SCENE EIGHT

The lights come up again. **Mr Forrester** *has gone. Up in the room,* **Mrs Forrester** *is organising the last stages of a move. The rooms are bare. The* **family** *carry their possessions in their arms and are on their way downstairs.* **Mrs Foster** *pokes her head out of her door. All this is happening while* **Helen** *narrates.*

HELEN *narrating* My mother decided we must move. She found a neat-looking terraced house with three bedrooms. There was no bathroom and the water closet was at the end of a grimy yard, but it was a house and the rent was only seventeen shillings a week. And then, of course, they went and bought a whole set of living-room furniture on what the loan sharks described as 'the easy payment system'.

MOTHER *without any regret at all* Goodbye, Mrs Foster.

Mrs Foster slams her door shut.

HELEN *narrating, as the family go off with their few possessions* I said 'What about beds? Beds are much more important.'

MOTHER *as she passes* **Helen** I've told you before. I'm not getting grubby secondhand stuff from Mr Moritz. I want nice new furniture in my front room. We might even manage a piano. Come on, Helen. Hurry up. And you're not carrying anything. You push Edward.

They go out, leaving **Helen** *with the pram.*

HELEN *narrating* So we went on sleeping on old boards and we went on covering ourselves with ragged coats, and coal and food were as scarce as ever. Nobody said a word about school. I carried on looking after Edward all day because my mother had to keep on working to pay off the tallyman. And so nothing changed except our address. Alan was nearly fourteen. They started talking about what he'd like to do when he left school. Nobody asked me what I'd like to do. 'As soon as they're sitting safely on the rock,' my old gentleman in the park had said, 'they'll reach down and haul you up.' But they didn't, and I was tired of hanging on in the hope that one day they might. I couldn't face things just going on and on and on. I was too tired.

*Slowly, **Helen** pushes the pram up the slope to the Pier Head and angles the pram so that **Edward** is looking out over the water.*

HELEN   *to Edward*   I'm going to leave you here, Edward. You'll be all right. Sit up, look. There's a good boy. There's the Birkenhead Ferry. See. You watch the boats. Somebody will find you. I've written your address inside the hood. You just watch the boats.

*Helen then goes over to the edge of the Pier Head. The pram should be angled so that **Edward** couldn't possibly see her. She leans for a moment on the railings. We hear the sounds of the river: gulls, boats etc. An old **sailor** is strolling up the slope. **Helen** looks round, and, failing to see the sailor, makes up her mind and slips under the railings. She balances precariously on the very edge of the Pier Head. Then she closes her eyes. After a moment we hear her softly counting.*

HELEN   One . . . two . . . three . . .

*But the **sailor** has spotted her.*

SAILOR   Here, hang on! What in the name of God . . . !

*Helen bends her knees to spring. The **sailor** grabs at her cardigan and pulls her back from the edge.*

SAILOR   Mother in heaven, you gave us a fright. Hey, come on . . . come on . . . don't pass out on me . . . Here, have a swig of this . . . warm you up.

*Helen is shaking and crying. The **sailor** holds her and pulls a small bottle of rum from his pocket and forces her to drink. It makes her splutter.*

SAILOR   Jesus, girl, you can't be that desperate to get out of Liverpool, can you? And even if you are . . . here, have another   *And he offers her another swig*   . . . Even if you are, I promise you there's better ways out than trying to swim across the Mersey.   *He has taken off his coat and wraps it round her shoulders*   You sit there a minute. I'll see if I can find you a cup of tea. There's a canteen across the road.

HELEN *narrating* He was quite right. There *were* better ways out of Liverpool. What a stupid thing to do. And I had *still* been expecting all the time that someone would wave a magic wand and change everything. No, if I wanted change, then I began to realise that I'd have to make it happen myself.

SCENE NINE

The lights fade. When the lights come up again, **Mrs Forrester** *is in the new house.* **Alan** *is sitting at the table doing his homework.* **Brian** *and* **Tony** *are grizzling at each other.* **Fiona** *sits hugging her teddy bear. The pram is in the room.* **Helen** *stands facing her mother, who is slicing a loaf of bread and is clearly very angry.*

MOTHER Where on earth have you been, Helen Forrester? The children came home from school hours ago. I come back and find poor Alan's had to cook supper for them, and he's had to put Avril to bed.

HELEN Why not? Do him good. He's old enough.

MOTHER He may be old enough, young lady, but he's got better things to do with his time. He's got homework to do.

HELEN I've got better things to do with my time as well. I shall be out two evenings a week from now on. You won't mind, will you, Alan?

MOTHER Two evenings a week? What are you talking about? Get that pram out of the way. Oh, for goodness sake, Tony, stop whining.

HELEN I've just enrolled myself at night school. For the commercial course.

MOTHER You've done what?! Don't turn your back when I'm talking to you. You've done what?

HELEN It doesn't matter any more. I'm fifteen. They can ask my age as much as they want. I can't think why I didn't realise that before.

MOTHER And what about the money? Where will you get that from?

HELEN I don't know. But I'll get it. I've borrowed all the books I need from the library. All I want is 2/6 for the

61

course fee. And then I'll try to win a scholarship to cover next year's fees. The teacher says there are several scholarships *Pointedly* Open to anyone.

MOTHER *taking the point* I see. How much did you say?

HELEN I'll get the money. I'll beg for it if I have to.

MOTHER You will not.

HELEN I will.

MOTHER Two shillings and sixpence?

HELEN Yes.

MOTHER You'd better pass me my bag, then. Over there. Don't gawp. *Helen passes her the bag.* **Mrs Forrester** *finds the money and gives it to* **Helen** It's the tally man's money. He'll just have to wait, won't he? I suppose I'll just about manage to make it up next week.

Helen comes to the front of the stage. She holds the money in her hand.

HELEN Two shillings and sixpence. Look. Suddenly. So easily. I couldn't believe it. I held it tight in case they suddenly realised they'd run out of cigarettes or it turned out my father had spent his tram fare on something else. And I wouldn't let her make me feel guilty for taking the tallyman's money. It was mine. It was. They owed it to me. And now I could start on a journey that would take me a lot further than the ferry ride to Birkenhead. I was on my way.

The lights fade.

THE END

STAGING THE PLAY

The action of *Twopence to Cross the Mersey* flows smoothly among a number of different locations and incidents, linked by Helen's narration. Because the audience have Helen to describe settings and move the action on, there is no need for a stage set which contains precise representations of each location in the play. It would be possible to stage the play using only two main acting areas: one for Mrs Foster's house, including the stairs, hall, the main room and the children's bedroom; the other for the street scenes, the park and so on. Movable props, such as doors, a park bench, etc. can be used to indicate specific locations, although it might be best to keep props and scenery changes to a minimum, so as not to hold up the movement of the play.

Lighting can also be used to define a particular scene, whether it is set indoors or out, day or night. Effective lighting will also serve to focus attention on the scene being played while another one is being set up. This will work well in those scenes where Helen steps out of a scene to address the audience directly while other actors are still on stage.

Although the cast is at first sight a large one, if necessary the piece can be played by doubling many of the minor characters. Also, it may not be necessary to have the whole family on stage when they are not directly involved in dialogue or the action.

Although Helen is the central character in the play, it is important that the other characters, do not fade into the background. Try to give each of the children a fully rounded personality. This can come out in their movements as much as in their lines. Bring out the despair and bewilderment of Mr Forrester and the bitterness of Mrs Forrester. Their relationship to each other and the rest of the characters is vital to the sense of the play and the action of the plot.

Costumes are best kept simple; elaborate costume changes will only hold up the movement of the action. The decline of the family's fortunes can be shown simply and effectively by discarding garments such as coats and hats, and by costumes that can gradually become more threadbare during the play.

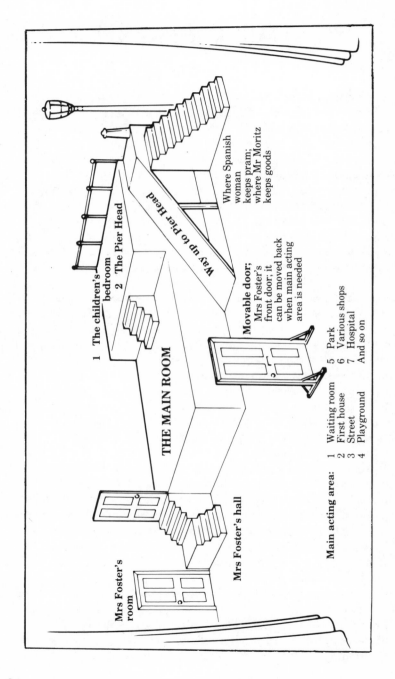

1 The children's bedroom
2 The Pier Head

THE MAIN ROOM

Way up to Pier Head

Where Spanish woman keeps pram; where Mr Moritz keeps goods

Movable door: Mrs Foster's front door; it can be moved back when main acting area is needed

Mrs Foster's room

Mrs Foster's hall

Main acting area:
1 Waiting room
2 First house
3 Street
4 Playground
5 Park
6 Various shops
7 Hospital
And so on

WORK ON AND AROUND THE SCRIPT

Drama

1 Favourites and scapegoats

Organisation: Work in a group of two or three. The Forresters have not yet lost their money and are still living a comfortable life in the south of England.

Situation: One of the group is Mrs Forrester. She is talking to one or two of her well-off friends about Helen, her eldest child. How does she describe Helen? What ideas has she for Helen's future? Do Mrs Forrester's friends have any different opinions or attitudes about the girl?

Opening line: MRS FORRESTER: It's hard to believe that Helen is really my daughter.

2 Upstairs, downstairs

Organisation: Work in a group of three. Decide who will be each of the three servants the Forresters had when they were well-off – Mary Anne the parlourmaid, the Cook or the Nanny.

Situation: Each of you has noticed that things have been changing in the Forrester household. You are already owed a month's wages, and now you have heard rumours that the family has lost all its money. How do you respond to this news and what action do you decide to take?

Opening line: MARY ANNE: I'm not going to stand for it. I want my wages!

3 Reminders of the past

Organisation: Work with a partner. One of you is either Mr or Mrs Forrester. The other is one of the children.

Situation: Avril brought her teddy bear with her to Liverpool. Imagine that you also have some special item with you which means a great deal to you. It is your only link with your past life. Although it may not be very valuable, if it were pawned it could bring in a few pennies to buy food for the family. The parent tries to persuade you to part with your special object so that it can be taken to the pawnbroker.

Opening line: PARENT: Don't be selfish, you're not a child any more.

Development: Later, create the scene (with your partner as the pawnbroker) in which the parent tries to pawn the special object.

4 Happy dreams

Organisation: Work in a small group of three or four.

Situation: Helen must have sometimes dreamt of her life as it was before the family went to Liverpool. Create a happy dream of her past for Helen, using sound and movement, to build a dream-like atmosphere. Contrast the mood of the dream with the kind of conditions she finds herself in when she wakes up.

5 The street

Organisation: Work with a partner. One of you is the Forrester's landlady. The other is a friend of hers who lives in the same street.

Situation: The neighbour is curious about the arrival of the Forresters. They are not like the other families in the street. Mrs Forrester keeps herself aloof. What can the neighbour find out about the Forresters?

Opening line: NEIGHBOUR: Who do they think they are? Royalty?

6 A helping hand

Organisation: Work with a partner. One of you is either the Spanish woman, Mr Moritz the pawnbroker, or the young policeman who paid for the baby's milk. The other is a friend or relative, or business partner.

Situation: You are trying to explain why you felt you must help the Forresters. Perhaps the person you are talking to is not so kind, and believes that charity begins at home.

Opening line: FRIEND OR RELATION: People take advantage of your good nature. You won't get any thanks for it.

---

7 A good neighbour?

Organisation: Work with a partner. One of you is a neighbour of the Forresters, and the other is a member of the family.

Situation: Although you are poor yourself, you feel there is something you can do to help the Forresters. Decide what kind of help you will offer, and which member of the family you will approach. Your partner can then take on the role of that person.

Opening line: THE NEIGHBOUR: I hope you won't think I'm intruding, but I couldn't help noticing that you are having problems.

---

8 A face from the past

Organisation: Work in a small group of three or four. One person in the group is a friend of the Forresters' grandmother, who lives across the Mersey. The rest of the group are members of the family.

Situation: The aunt has accidentally met Mrs Forrester and some of the children in the street. Helen's mother tries to pretend that everything is fine, but the aunt can't help noticing how thin, dirty and poorly clothed the children are.

Opening line: FRIEND: Celia, I hardly recognised you.

Development: That evening, the friend tells the grandmother about the unexpected meeting. She tries to get the grandmother to change her mind and help the family.

Opening line: FRIEND: You'll never guess who I met today . . .

---

9 A lost opportunity

Organisation: Work in a group of three. Two of you are Mr and Mrs Forrester, the other is the head teacher of the school that Helen attends for a few weeks.

Situation: Helen's parents have received the news of her scholarship to the Art College. They are now visiting the school to explain why she can't possibly accept. How honest will they be? Will they explain the truth of their situation or will they invent excuses?

Opening line: HEADTEACHER: You must be very proud of your daughter. She has a real future.

---

10 Deserving poor

Organisation: Work in a group of five or six. You are the Committee who look after the School Benevolent Fund. One of you is the person who met Mr Forrester and encouraged him to apply for help.

Situation: The Committee are meeting to decide what should be done about the Forresters' application for assistance. You may all have different views about the kinds of people who deserve your help.

Opening line: COMMITTEE MEMBER: I can think of a great many more deserving cases who need our help. After all, we don't have unlimited resources.

---

11 In later life

Organisation: Work with a partner. One of you is Helen and the other is Helen's mother.

Situation: Twenty years have passed since the action of the play. Helen is now an independent woman, earning her own living. She is visiting her elderly mother. How has their relationship changed? Does Helen still bear a grudge against her mother for the way she was treated as a child?

Opening line: MOTHER: I remember how difficult you were as a child . . .

---

12 Talking across time

Organisation: Work in a group of two or three. One of you is Helen and the other(s) are teenagers from the 1980s.

Situation: Imagine that you have managed to communicate with Helen, who is still in the 1930s. What would you tell her about your lives in the 1980s? What would she find

strange or different? What advice or help could you give
her in her situation?

Opening line: HELEN: Life must be really easy for you . . .

Writing

1   Imagine that you are either Helen or Alan. You keep a
diary. Write one entry for a day before your life changed,
when your family were well-off, and one entry for the day on
which you came to Liverpool on the train to start a new life.

2   Helen and Alan's school friends have heard something
about the disaster which has happened to the family. Imagine
you are one of these friends. Write a letter to either Helen or
Alan. How will you show without hurting their feelings that
you know what has happened to the family and that you feel
sympathy for them?

3   The Forrester children had a difficult time at the school in
Liverpool. Think of an incident which might have happened to
them in school. Then imagine you are one of the teachers in
the school, and write a report on the children's behaviour.

4   Imagine that you are a newspaper reporter. You are
writing an article about unemployed people in Liverpool. You
were at Lime Street Station when the Forrester family
arrived. Write the first part of your article and include a
description of the Forresters. Imagine that you have
interviewed them for your paper, and include some remarks
they might have made.

5   Write a poem in which you compare the two lives (before
and after the move to Liverpool) led by the Forrester children.
Work at creating an atmosphere for each part of the poem.
Try to show how the children felt to have such a change in
their way of life.

6   One of the ways in which Mrs Forrester managed to get
some money was by writing begging letters to well-off friends
from her past. How do you think she might have explained
things to them? Write your version of one of these letters.
How can you make your situation sound really serious
without putting people off by describing the real squalor in
which the family are living?

7 On their first Christmas in Liverpool, the Forresters had a rather strange Christmas dinner. Imagine that you have heard about the Forresters and have decided to send the family a Christmas present. Decide whether you would give them a practical gift or something luxurious. Write to them, explaining what your present is.

BACKGROUND TO THE PLAY

The Depression

Twopence to Cross the Mersey is set in a period of history
known as the Depression. What happened to make these
years so bleak for many people?

In 1929 the New York stock market on Wall Street
collapsed. The collapse ruined banks, businesses and private
investors in a matter of days. People suddenly became very
poor. This financial disaster was called the 'Wall Street
Crash', and its effects were soon felt around the world.

Unemployment

Unemployment rose rapidly after the Wall Street Crash as
lack of world demand for coal, steel and cotton – Britain's
traditional industries forced manufacturers to lay off workers.
By 1931 unemployment stood at 3 million.

When people were in work, they paid a weekly sum into an
insurance fund, to which the government and the employers
also contributed. If someone lost their job, they were entitled
to a weekly sum which was paid out of the fund. This was
known as Unemployment Benefit or the 'dole'. In 1931, the
amounts available were:

Male unemployed	**17 shillings**
Female unemployed	**15 shillings**
Dependent wife	**9 shillings**
Each child	**2 shillings**

(Note: The money system used in the 1930s was pounds (£),
shillings (*s.*) and pence (*d.*). There were 12 pence in a shilling,
and 20 shillings in a pound.

Because of the large and growing number of unemployed,
the fund was running into debt by 1931. To save money, a
number of measures were introduced to cut the cost of the
'dole'. A man's benefit was cut to 15*s*. 3*d*., and that of his wife
to 8*s*. Women who married found that the contributions to the

fund which they had paid while single were now disallowed. Also benefit was only paid if the claimant had worked for thirty weeks out of the previous two years.

The most important change was to limit to six months the period in which benefit was paid. After that time, the unemployed had to apply to the local Poor Law authorities for their money. To get further benefit, unemployed people had to face a thorough investigation of how poor they were, including their home and their relatives. This was the hated Means Test. The Poor Law investigators could check on savings, furniture, and earnings of the children of the unemployed. They would then reduce the amount paid if they could find a reason for this. Because it was a local, not a national system, the payments varied from place to place. In *Twopence to Cross the Mersey*, Mr Forrester is paid the Surrey rate of relief, even though the family has moved to Liverpool.

People resented having to accept charity, and they resented the prying activities of the Poor Law investigators. Worst of all, the Means Test almost always led to a cut in relief payments for the unemployed. Here are some examples of the worst excessess of the Means Test:

- An unemployed man with a wife and two children had his allowance reduced to 20s. per week because they shared a house with the man's mother-in-law.
- Two men in their twenties had their claim disallowed because their mother had a war widow's pension.
- A miner with a wife and six children had his payments stopped after it was discovered he had £15 saved up in the Co-op.

Often, furniture, clothing and other household effects had to be pawned or sold before people were able to claim their 'dole' from the Poor Law authorities. The Test forced people to spend their hard-won savings. Also, because it took into account any earnings the children of the house might have, it encouraged the break-up of families.

However, for some people, the 1930s were not a time of depression and the dole. For those in work wages remained fairly steady. Some people enjoyed a rise in living standards and the gap between the 'haves' and 'have-nots' had become very wide. Even after 'recovery' in 1934–5, the number of Britain's unemployed stayed at around 1.5 million until the outbreak of war in 1939.

Unemployed men looking for work in the local papers.

Life on 'the dole' in the 1930s

The end of this month will make it two years since I worked last. During this period we lived (that is myself, wife and three children) first on 32 shillings a week and since on 29s. 3d. a week transitional payment.

On the latter scale the family budget works out like this:

	s.	d.
Rent	11	0
coal (1½ cwt)	2	9
gas (cooking and washing)	1	2
light (electric)	1	0
club subscription (boots, clothing,		
crockery, bed-clothing etc.)	3	0
burial insurance		9
groceries (bread, tea, sugar etc.)	6	6
	26	2
balance	3	1
	29	3

The balance has to provide bacon, eggs, milk, meat, cereal, greengroceries etc. – in fact, has to buy everything that goes towards making a meal outside of bread, margarine, and a cup of tea, for a family of five all the week.

Just work it out. Multiply a family of five by three meals a day and by seven days a week. The result is 105 individual meals to be provided out of 37 pence! That is less than a halfpenny a meal. This means that we live mostly on tea and toast.

This diet has resulted in recurrent illness. The youngest child has had pneumonia three times since February of last year. She is now suffering from bronchitis, and according to the doctor, is probably developing TB.

The oldest child was in hospital last month with pneumonia. It was out one week and has now gone back again. I myself have only been signed off 'fit' today after an illness lasting a month.

The rent has been missed to meet the extra expenses that always crop up during sickness. And now a registered letter has come from the corporation with one week's notice to quit!

(from Fenner Brockway, *Hungry England*)

Drama
Life after the Means Test

Organisation: Work in groups of three to four. Two of you will
be the husband and wife described in 'Life on the dole'
from Fenner Brockway's book. The other one or two will
be friends or neighbours.

Situation: The family of five has been living on 32*s.* a week
while the man has been unemployed. However, they have
just been told that as from next week their benefit will be
reduced to 29*s.* 3*d.* Script and act out a conversation
between the husband, wife and friends or neighbours.

Opening line: WIFE: The man came to investigate us
yesterday.

This poem is based on the carol 'Away in a Manager'. The 'two
shillings' referred to is the allowance given to an unemployed
man to feed and clothe each of his children.

A carol
Oh hush thee, my baby,
They cradle's in pawn:
No blankets to cover thee
Cold and forlorn.
The stars in the bright sky
Look down and are dumb
At the heir of the ages
Asleep in a slum.

The hooters are blowing,
No heed let him take;
When baby is hungry
'Tis best not to wake.
Thy mother is crying,
Thy dad's on the dole:
Two shillings a week is
The price of a soul.

C. DAY LEWIS, 1935

Drama

Nativity

Organisation: Work in a small group. Create a scene from a
modern-day nativity play, set in the 1930s. Let a poor
family take the place of Mary, Joseph and Jesus. What
parallels can you find for the inn, the stable, the
shepherds and the wise men?

Development: If each group chooses a different part of the
story to present, you can link the scenes together to cover
the whole story.

The hunger marches

During the 1930s there were many occasions when the
unemployed marched to petition against unemployment and
the hated Means Test. The most famous of these marches took
place in 1936. The unemployed ship-builders of Jarrow on
Tyneside walked 300 miles to London to beg the government
to introduce new industries to their area.

The marchers were led by their MP, Ellen Wilkinson. They
attracted a good deal of sympathy and some hostility on their
journey south. The march became one of the most enduring
symbols of the Depression, but it achieved little for the people
of Jarrow. The marchers returned as heroes, but found that
their dole had been reduced. The reason given was that when
they were on the march they were unavailable for work.

Malnutrition and idleness gave the marchers a refined, almost
delicate, look. Their slight bodies were covered by dark,
clothing club suits and each wore a roll of mackintosh across
the chest and over the shoulder like a bandolier. The men wore
cloth caps. They marched gravely in step to the sound of the
mouth organs and with the dimunitive Ellen Wilkinson at their
head. The progress of the marchers was grave, almost sedate.
The miseries of the Depression had made them unnaturally
reserved and reflective. Not many days had passed before fresh
air and the sheer delight of being necessary brought a
transformation to the wan faces that was little short of
miraculous. By the time the men got to Sheffield they had lost
their humiliated look and had instead a certain nervous poise.

(from Ronald Blythe,
The Age of Illusion, 1919–1940 Hamish Hamilton, 1963)

The Jarrow marchers on their way to London.

Drama

Looking on

Organisation: Work with a partner. It is 1936. Both of you are well-off people with good jobs, living in London.

Situation: You have been watching the arrival of the Jarrow marchers. One of you knows a little about the plight of the unemployed in the North-East and is sympathetic about their hardships. The other person believes that those on the dole could find work if they really wanted to, and that many of the marchers are idle and shiftless. Can each of you convince the other of your own point of view?

Opening line: WELL-OFF PERSON: I just don't believe this nonsense about unemployment. Why, I can't find a gardener to come in once a week!

77

Food

The Forresters' meagre diet of bread, potatoes, sugar and tea
was shared by many families during this period.

> Not only the unemployed, but also the lowest wage earners,
> were just able to keep going by eating large quantities of bread
> and potatoes. The old diet of the poor was back again – white
> bread, margarine, jam, sugar and tea, together with potatoes
> and dried fish. The fish and chip shop was the working-man's
> best friend. Milk was only too often something that came out of
> a tin. Fresh vegetables, apart from potatoes, were bought
> sparingly. Meat was a weekend indulgence. Late on Saturday
> night the prices went down and you could buy some sort of cut
> cheap.

Henry Fell described his life in a small town in Cumberland.
Their family, though poor, was not short of food, except when
his father was unemployed:

> We didn't have very much to eat those six weeks but there was
> plenty of bread and a lot of broth every day, cheap vegetables
> and a pennyworth of bones at the butcher's and in those days
> there was quite a lot of meat on some of the bones.

Melvyn Bragg, *Speak for England*, Secker & Warburg, 1976

THEMES AND ISSUES IN THE PLAY

The scholarship

In the play Helen regards school as a way of escaping from the poverty and drudgery of her life at home. In the 1930s the school-leaving age was 14. Passing the scholarship – the entrance exam for free places at the local grammar school – was the only way a child of poor parents could hope to get a secondary education.

Classroom scene, 1935. The cost of school uniform could be a real problem for poor families.

Many poor children won scholarships and could not afford to take them up. Their parents could not sacrifice the £1 a week the children might earn if they left school and get a job at 14, or they could not find the money necessary for a school uniform and other extras. Increasingly, young people took advantage of evening classes, as Helen does in the play, as they realised that an education could mean escape from the poverty and hopelessness of their parents' lives.

In the extract below, Phyllis Wilmott, who had recently changed schools, did not get the scholarship she had hoped for. She got a 'free place' at a local grammar school, but this did not cover expenses.

My satisfaction was rapidly destroyed as I listened to Mum. She was extremely alarmed at the duplicated list of clothes and equipment she had been given by Miss Higgs, the Headmistress. It was clear to her that it was going to cost pounds to 'set me up', and that would certainly not be the end of it. The more anxiously I urged that we could manage somehow, the more certain she became that the whole idea of me going at all was impossible. Fed up with my attempts alternately to argue and plead with her, she commanded 'Shut up. I shall have to speak to your father.'

When Dad came home, he found us both with long faces. Mum's face showed all the worry she felt; mine, that I was on the brink of tears. Mum explained the situation as she saw it, I interrupted and said but, please Dad, I want to go so much. Mum turned on me bitterly: 'You want to go, but it's me who'll have to pinch and scrape to keep you there.' We all knew this was the truth and, defeated, I fell silent. To hide my misery I put my arms on the table. The heavy pause was broken by Mum's voice: 'Well?' she asked. I looked up. The deep-set, saddened brown eyes stared intently at Dad, carrying some highly-charged message I could not fathom. Terse and unsmiling, not looking at either of us, Dad said, 'Let her go'.

Phyllis Wilmott, *Growing up in a London Village*, Peter Owen, 1979

Not everyone was as lucky as Phyllis. Norman Fell describes how he sat for the scholarship examination which would have taken him to the grammar school:

We were sitting for the exam and I went in the morning, and there was a teacher, Mabel Briggs. She was a wonderful teacher and I were in her class. And she said, prior to starting the exams, she said, Now you must concentrate because I think you've a good chance of going to the Grammar School. So we had the first part of the exams in the morning and oh I tried hard, and I felt I was doing exceptionally well. Until I went home, dinnertime. And my elder brother said, Under no circumstances must you pass for a scholarship because, he says, if you do, we'll never be able to clothe you to go to that school. And when I went back in the afternoon I just didn't try . . . And that is the position. When Mabel Briggs, the school mistress, said, what have you been doing this afternoon? When the exam results were known she said that she knew there was something wrong, and the wrong part about it were that I didn't try at all, because I knew the fact was that I wouldn't be able to go – I couldn't dress to go to that school.

I regretted very much that I didn't get the scholarship.

Melvyn Bragg, *Speak for England*, Secker and Warburg, 1976

Drama

1 Extra expenses

Organisation: Work with a partner. One of you is a teenager in the 1930s. The other is a schoolteacher.

Situation: The teenager has been asked to go on a school trip, and knows that it will be almost impossible for the family to afford this extra expense. The teacher explains how important and enjoyable the trip will be. How will you explain that it will be difficult for you to go?

Opening line: TEACHER: I want you to take this letter home to your parents.

2 Leaving school

Organisation: Work in a group of three or four. One of you is an unemployed parent; the other two are teenagers, the eldest brother and sister in a large family. If there are four of you, the extra person can be another parent or relative.

Situation: The parent is finding it impossible to manage to pay for food and rent for the family. Both the eldest children are at the grammar school. It is necessary for the girl to leave school and take a job in a shop. How will the parent break the news to her? Why has the girl been chosen to leave school? How will the other members of the family react?

Opening line: PARENT: I've got to talk to you both.

Discussion
1 In the play, Helen feels that her parents refuse to take seriously her longing for an education. Do you think a good education is as important for a girl as it is for a boy?

2 What do you think the best school leaving age would be? At present it is 16.

3 Many people in Britain choose to pay for their children's education. Do you think this is a good thing? What are the basics which people should get from an education?

4 Uniform was an expensive item for parents in the 1930s. Should school uniform be compulsory? Does your school have a uniform? What rules are there in your school about pupils' appearance?

Women's work
In the 1930s, it was assumed that women would do all the domestic work. In the play it is Helen who is expected to take the responsibility of looking after the children, which means she isn't allowed to go to school. When women worked outside the home, they did not receive equal pay with men for equal work.

In the 19th century, many working-class girls had become servants. However, in the early 20th century, the growing number of shops and factories made it possible for more and more girls to find an alternative to domestic service.

For middle-class girls, it was almost impossible to get married *and* have a career. Women who became teachers or civil servants had to give up their jobs if they married.

Women working in a razor factory, 1935.

In the 1930s, if a girl was the daughter of a low-paid or unemployed worker, she couldn't afford new clothes or make-up. If she did find a job, the Means Test might deprive her father of his Unemployment Benefit.

For Helen, then, the future doesn't seem to hold out much promise through work or through marriage.

Physically, it was a harder life for the wife of a long-term unemployed man than it was for him. She was the one who washed and cleaned without soap, who wheedled fat out of the butcher to melt down for fried bread for the children's breakfast, who patched and re-patched clothes so that they had something to wear for school. But spiritually, the wives were undefeated. It was their battle. They could keep the children fed and cared for and the household running by their own ceaseless effort and grim endurance. So long as the mother did not give up, the home was secure. Her status increased as that of the unemployed father diminished. In a culture in which the man's standing and his weapon of authority had been the living wage he brought home, he was now completely disarmed.

The only thing he could do was women's work. There was always plenty of that about. Women could get a job twice as easily as men, because they could do domestic work, scrubbing, cleaning, washing and baby-minding. When the wife took on paid work of this kind, it meant that the unemployed husband had to stay at home and do all that she used to do.

In households where the breadwinner was female, she gradually became accepted as the decision-maker.

Ruth Adam, *A Woman's Place,*
1910–1975, Chatto and Windus, 1975

> A working-class bachelor is a rarity, and as long as a man is married unemployment makes comparatively little alteration in his way of life. His home is impoverished but it is still a home, and it is noticeable everywhere that the anomalous position created by unemployment – the man being out of work while the woman's work continues as before – has not altered the relative status of the sexes. In a working-class home it is the man who is the master. Practically never, for instance, in a working-class home, will you see the man doing a stroke of the housework. Unemployment has not changed this convention, which on the face of it seems a little unfair. The man is idle from morning to night but the woman is as busy as ever – more so, indeed, because she has to manage with less money. Yet, so far as my experience goes the women do not protest. I believe that they, as well as the men, feel that a man would lose his manhood if, merely because he was out of work, he developed into a 'Mary Ann'.

Discussion

1   Would you agree with George Orwell that it seems 'a little unfair' for the woman in a household to do all the housework even though the man has nothing to do? Do you think that men who do housework become 'Mary Anns'? and lose their manhood?

2   Do you think the breadwinner in a family should become the decision-maker? What would happen if the only people working in the family were teenage children?

3   How is the housework allocated in your family? What jobs do the females in the family take on? Which jobs are done by the males? Is the arrangement a good one? Is there anything you would like to change about it?

4   In the play, Helen feels that she, as the eldest daughter, has to carry too much of the responsibility for the children and the housework. Who takes on different responsibilities in your family? Are there any areas of family life that *you* are responsible for?

Drama

1   Lending a hand

Organisation: Work with a partner. One of you is an unemployed man like those described in the extracts above. The other is his wife, or a female relation who feels that he should make a contribution to the work of the household. How can you persuade him to help.

Situation: It is the end of a very long day. The woman of the household has returned home to find the unemployed man sitting in a chair by the fire.

Opening line: MAN: What's for supper?

Young and unemployed

The Depression affected the lives of many young men and women. In a book called *Love on the Dole*, Walter Greenwood used his own experiences of unemployment to describe the hardships of the hungry 1930s. The book was an instant success and was turned into a play. In the extract below, Harry Hardcastle is out of work – he has too much time on his hands and not enough money.

A man of leisure in the 1930s

> There was a dull vacuity in his eyes nowadays; he became listless, hard of hearing, saying 'Eh?' when anybody asked him a question.
> Nothing to do with time; nothing to spend; nothing to do tomorrow nor the day after; nothing to wear; can't get married. A living corpse; a unit of the spectral army of three million lost men.
> Hands in pockets, shoulders hunched, he would slink round by the by-streets to the billiard hall, glad to be somewhere out

of the way of the public gaze, anyplace where there were no
girls to see him in his threadbare jacket and patched overalls.
Stealing into the place like a shadow to seat himself in a corner
of one of the wall seats to watch the prosperous young men who
had jobs and who could afford billiards, cigarettes and good
clothes.

At other times his heart would vomit at the thought of the
billiard hall. He would saunter about the streets, aimlessly;
kick at a tin can lying in the gutter, shoo an alley cat: 'Pshhhh!
Gerrout of it!', hum or whistle some daft jazz tune, stand
transfixed at street corners, brain a blank. Then, waking to a
deep hungering for a smoke, would drift inevitably to the
billiard hall. Or he might forget where he was going; have his
attention diverted by the play-bills of the picture theatres;
half-naked tarts being mauled by dark-haired men in evening
clothes. Daft. Sometimes there were interesting police notices
in the chip shop window: 'Lost, a Toy Dog. £5 Reward.' Jesus! A
fiver for a blasted mongrel. Go'n look for it, Harry. A fiver,
though! 'Wanted for Murder'. A fellow who's murdered a bank
clerk for money: 'All y've got t'do Harry, is t'sneak into a bank,
land the clerk a good 'un over the head and then help yourself'.

Money.

'Ah may as well be in bloody prison.' He suddenly wakened to
the fact that he was a prisoner. The walls of the shops, houses
and places of amusement were his prison walls: lacking money
to buy his way into them, the doors were all closed against him.
That was the function of doors and walls; they were there to
keep out those who hadn't any money. He was a prisoner at
large.

Walter Greenwood, *Love on the Dole*, 1933

Drama

1 Contrasts

Organisation: Work with a partner. One of you is
    unemployed, like the young man in this extract. The
    other is a close friend from school who has been lucky
    enough to find a job.

Situation: The two friends meet. It is obvious that they are
    leading very different lives. What can they find to talk
    about? Does the friend with the job boast about it, or try
    to play down the fact? Does his friend try to make being
    on the dole sound positive?

Opening line: FRIEND: So what are you doing these days?

2 Daydreaming

Organisation: Work in a small group.

Situation: Harry, in this extract, imagines situations in which his fortunes might change for the better. Create a fantasy scene in which Harry has a stroke of good luck – perhaps finding the lost dog and getting a large reward, or helping someone who gives him a wonderful job. Since your scene is not realistic, you can exaggerate the incidents and language to create the effect you want.

Unemployment in the 1980s
Many unemployed youths are tempted towards crime in the 1980s, as Harry Hardcastle was in the 1930s.

Money is giving me a hard time. My parents help me out, but I feel bad about it. My mum was a nurse, but she's not working now. My dad's a carpenter, but he's been complaining he can't even afford a new pair of boots. He keeps pestering me to find a job. I say a job where? The careers office is always offering me rubbish jobs, the Jobcentre sends a hundred people before you so you got no chance. But I still go for interviews just for something to do. Now I hardly got no money for to take me anywhere. I come here and play a game of pool, I walk around the streets, I go home and play music, I get fed up. I got no clothes. The fashion now is dressing nice. It's just a rat race you just can never win. You got no money, they don't want to know you. Crime? I think of that the whole time, robbing banks, but I got no courage to go and do it. If I see a woman walking up the road, I always think of taking her handbag, but then I think, it might be my mother and I don't do it.

Paul Harrison, *Inside the Inner City*, Penguin, 1983

Discussion
1 What are some of the similarities between Harry's life on the dole in the 1930s and Paul's in the 1980s? Are there any differences?

2 'I'd rather live in the thirties than now. I'd rather be fighting in the war than be like I am now. I wish I was still in school. If I could just stop time, and be sixteen.'
Steve Capes, unemployed father of three small children

Would you feel the same as Steve Capes if you were
unemployed? Why?

Unemployed girls

The unemployed girls I met seemed, for the most part, less
deeply demoralised than the boys: as they are usually expected
to shoulder a share of the housework, they have more to occupy
their time than boys; their expectations of life are less heavily
geared to career and earning power; and the option is open to
them to resolve the problem of inability to afford a night out by
going out with boys who are in work. Even for them,
unemployment remains a distasteful, distressing experience.
Caroline Weymouth, a pretty eighteen-year-old, was still in
her dressing-gown at 3 in the afternoon when I called at her
parents' home on Nightingale Estate.

'I always wanted to be a ground stewardess, but the careers
teacher told me I hadn't done well enough at school and the
only job I could do was shop work. I got a job at British Home
Stores but I chucked it in. Some of the customers who came in
treated you like muck. I am looking for another job but I can't
afford to go for the interviews. The employers have got the pick
of the bunch now. They want 'O' Levels and CSE even to work
in a sweet shop.

'It costs so much now for a night out that I can't afford to go
unless the man pays. But I don't like that, I'd rather pay myself
so they can't make out that I owe them anything.'

Paul Harrison, *Inside the Inner City*, Penguin, 1983.

Drama

1 Explanations

Organisation: Work with a partner. One of you is Caroline,
the other is the careers teacher at her school.

Situation: Caroline has come for her final career interview.
How does the teacher explain to her what her *real* job
prospects are? Does Caroline accept these facts easily?

Opening line: CAROLINE: I'd like to be a stewardess.

2 Pictures of Caroline

Organisation: Work in a group of four or five.

Situation: Create several tableaux (frozen pictures) of
   Caroline's life, including her ambitions, her attitude at
   school, her unsuccessful first job, and the reality of her life
   on the dole.

3 Going out

Organisation: Work with a partner. One of you is Caroline, or
   a girl in the same circumstances. The other is a friend,
   also unemployed.

Situation: The friend has met two boys with good jobs. The
   boys have asked the two girls out for the evening to an
   expensive restaurant, and the friend is eager to accept.
   How will Caroline react to the invitation? Can her friend
   persuade her to accept?

Opening line: FRIEND: It's ages since you've been out
   anywhere.

Discussion
1 Paul Harrison seems to suggest that girls' unequal share
of the household chores is a good thing, and that
unemployment is less serious for girls. Do you agree?

2 Do you think that girls had different expectations in the
1930s? How have such expectations changed in the 1980s?

3 Is it always appropriate for a boy to pay for a girl when he
takes her out? Why do you think that Caroline, in the extract
above, would rather pay for herself?

Writing
1 Imagine that you are a teacher at Caroline's school, and
write a report on her attitudes and behaviour, based on what
we learn about her in the extract above.

2 Write a letter to someone who holds the same views as
Paul Harrison. How can you make him see the other side of
the picture?

3 Write a short story entitled: 'The Day I got a Job'.

4 Create a cartoon-strip about a young person like Harry or Caroline who is living on the dole.

Further activities

1 Work in a group of three or four. Create part of a documentary for radio about the plight of the unemployed in the 1930s. Try to include 'interviews' with unemployed people and their families, using passages from this book. Write a script which will link the interviews with comment.

2 If you prefer, you could create a TV documentary, contrasting the unemployment of the 1930s with that of the 1980s. What similarities and contrasts can you find in the two situations? If you have access to a video camera, try to bring your programme to life, using classmates as the unemployed people of both eras.

3 Research your local area for information about the growth or decline of industries. How has the prosperity of the area changed? How many of the pupils in your school who left last year have found jobs? Make up a monologue on the subject of hope and despair.

4 If you were old enough to leave school and couldn't find a job, how much could you expect to get on the dole? What would your priorities be in spending the money? Where would you live? Use a tape or video recorder and get a cross-section of your friends' views.

5 It is predicted that in the near future we may have to adjust to a society in which many people are permanently unemployed. How would you organise things for a population who have a great deal of leisure time and perhaps not very much money? Discuss this, and present your suggestions in a short report to your MP or councillor.